THE TOOTHPICK AIRFORCE	

BUILD AND FLY...

THE FIRST FLYERS

ROBERT B. ELLIOTT

To Lalee

Robert B Elliott

Booger Red

BOOGER RED'S BOOKS

"Build and Fly THE FIRST FLYERS" is dedicated to the first to fly… the Wright Brothers, Wilbur and Orville, to Otto Lilienthal, Octave Chanute, Glen Curtiss, Louis Bleriot, Alberto Santos-Dumont, the Voisin Brothers to name just a few of the many who pioneered flight. It is also dedicated to the flyers of "Real Glider Replicas", the first book of THE TOOTHPICK AIRFORCE series, who made this book possible.

The photograph on the cover is from the collection of Jim Over of Crawford, Co. It is thought to be one of the first flights over Catalina Island and back, perhaps by Glen Martin in 1913.

ISBN: 0-9650751-2-5

BUILD AND FLY...
The First Flyers

When the Wright Brothers first flew at Kitty Hawk, men had glided with little or no control over the direction or duration of their flight; most of the time their goal was just to stay airborne. The Wright Brothers not only made one the first powered flights, they made controlled, powered flight a reality. The essential control surfaces were for the first time put together in a machine with the power and lift necessary to truly conquer the air. The fact that they had to teach themselves to use those control surfaces and actually fly, in only the briefest moments of flight, makes their accomplishment even grander.

The goal of <u>BUILD AND FLY THE FIRST FLYERS</u> is to help the reader construct flying glider replicas of the first aviation pioneers' aircraft. To accomplish this, a mastery of the actual workings of the control surfaces they pioneered is essential. The beauty of "THE TOOTHPICK AIRFORCE" concept is these gliders only fly when lift, balance, and the control surfaces are tuned properly, just like the real aircraft. This book provides a formula for combining those workings, just as the Wright brothers (and the other pioneers) did, but using just paper, paste, and toothpicks.

Wherever possible I have built into the text definitions that are required to understand the theory of flight. Each section is designed to provide its own reward for reading and following the instructions. The reward is a flying replica of one of the real pioneers of aviation aircraft.

SUPPLIES AND REQUIREMENTS

1. Scissors, the sharper the better!
2. Paper—20 lb is good, 24 lb is better. Various colors are available in both 20 and 24 lb and these can enhance aircraft appearance.
3. Toothpicks of the flat variety provide the best airframes. Flat toothpicks are available at most grocery stores. Square or round toothpicks may be useful.
4. Elmer's Glue-All is recommended.
5. Access to a copier, or a computer with a scanner and printer is helpful.
6. Large fingernail clippers, ruler, and protractor to measure angles.
7. Always cut on the solid lines, fold on the dotted lines!
8. Patience and persistence in equal measure.

THE TOOTHPICK AIRFORCE

BUILD AND FLY...
THE FIRST FLYERS

The oldest original flying aircraft in the U.S.A., at the time, taken at the Dupage County Airport, Il. in 1967. Photo by Bob Svoboda of Grand Junction, Colorado.

CONTENTS

Contents:

THE WRIGHT SOLUTION

We know now, flight is possible only when there is a balance between three absolute necessities: **lift**, **control**, and **thrust**. But in 1900 the Wright Brothers had to figure this out for themselves. These words have special meaning in aeronautics:

Lift - The component of the force exerted by the air on an airfoil, being opposite the force of gravity and causing an aircraft to stay in the air.

Control - To hold in restraint or check; to regulate; to govern.

Thrust - To push or drive with force.

When the Wright brothers set out to conquer the air, they had access to the writings of Otto Lilienthal, Octave Chanute, and other enthusiasts of flight. Lilienthal (pronounced Leel'yen-tahl), a German pioneer, had made more than 2,000 manned glider flights beginning in 1891. Octave Chanute (pronounced Shuh-noot) was an American engineer who also pioneered manned gliders. After years of study, Chanute published a group of papers under the title "Progress in Flying Machines." Chanute maintained correspondence with virtually all the important figures in aviation, European and American, including the Wrights. In fact, gliding was already a reality when the Wright brothers began their experiments. Control was vital, and certainly not perfected. This was clearly demonstrated by Lilienthal's death in a gliding accident in 1896.

The first wind tunnel gave the Wrights the data they needed to build wings with enough lift. For control, the Wright's added a tail, and later made it movable. They could work the tail as a rudder using guy-wires and a lever. This controlled the **yaw**, or turns and was a huge improvement.

An essential improvement was called "wing-warping," and gave the Wright brothers the control they needed to adjust the lift

The 1902 Wright glider with double tail and wing-warping. See gliders on p. 16.

See gliders on p. 16.

generated by either the right or left wings by the movement of control wires. In their first airplanes the control wires were attached to a harness that the flier would lie in like a sling. This was changed to a lever in 1908.

The lever (or sling harness) would warp the leading edge of the wings on one side of the airplane upward, while at the same time warping the opposite wings downward. By warping the leading edge of the wings upward, the angle of attack was increased, increasing lift on that side of the airplane while decreasing it on the other. This kept the airplane stable by adjusting for **roll**.

The word "airplane" was descriptive of the method of "lift" in which a plane (the wing) is lifted by the pressure of the air against the lower surface as the wing is pushed or propelled forward. All the Wright gliders were basically "hand launched." In 1902, the Wright brothers made over 700 glides. However, the Wrights continued to make improvements to their basic designs by testing them first on gliders. In 1911, Orville Wright made a record glide of nine and three quarter minutes that was not bested for 10 years.

Orville's 1911 glider had the "elevator" at the rear of the airplane.

Up and down control (**pitch**) was provided by what the Wrights called a "horizontal rudder," which was located at the front of the Wrights' first aircraft. Because these controlled the up and down, they became "elevators" on modern aircraft.

We so far have been unable to develop engines and propellers of appropriate size and weight for THE TOOTHPICK AIRFORCE. Fortunately the Wrights did for the real Kitty Hawk flyer.

The final challenge in fact to the Wright brothers was in developing their own engine, and an efficient propeller. **When the Wrights finally flew in December of 1903, they had finally mastered lift, control, and thrust!**
Definitions:
Stability—An airplane is stable if it flies straight and level, and can be righted if disturbed by a gust of wind or turbulence.

An airplane can be rotated to maintain stability (using the control surfaces) through three axes; lateral, vertical, and longitudinal. These motions are called yaw, pitch, and roll.
Yaw— the motion of the aircraft when it turns to the right or left.
Pitch— the motion of the aircraft when it points its nose at the ground to dive or upward to climb.
Roll— the motion when the aircraft's wings dip or are raised to one side.
Dihedral—the wing tips are higher than the wing roots.

Basic Training
With the Bleriot Model XI

In 1908 Louis Bleriot witnessed Wilbur Wright's first European demonstration of flight. Although Bleriot and others had "flown," it is generally now recognized that only the Wrights had mastered the air. Their performance included flying circles, figure eights, shallow climbs and dives, and clearly demonstrated controlled flight. Wright even carried passengers aloft!

Louis Bleriot's own aircraft, his Model VIII, had flown but showed control problems. Bleriot's aircraft used primitive ailerons on the wings which were causing him control difficulty.

Having witnessed the effectiveness of wing warping technology in the Wright Flyer, he modified his own aircraft.

In the Model XI, one of his most successful designs ever, Bleriot utilized "wing warping." This aircraft was produced and used from 1909 well into the First World War. There were several different versions because it was manufactured by different builders in France, Germany, Italy, and the United States and each builder made additions or improvements. Indeed, this was the case with aircraft from every successful designer. Copies (more or less) were literally made in backyards and garages, many times without the permission or license of the designer.

Bleriot XI in flight.

Some of the main license versions of Bleriot's famous designs are included for your building and flying pleasure.

The TA Bleriot XI with all seven paper parts is easy to build and tune.

THE TOOTHPICK AIRFORCE concept makes building and flying glider replicas of The First Flyers fun!

THE TOOTHPICK AIRFORCE (abbreviated TA throughout the book) Bleriot XI, because of its simplicity, is your flight trainer. It can be built and flown with as few as three paper parts, or the other four parts may be added easily for a more authentic replica.

3

About the Bleriot:

Bleriot Model XI (1909 Channel Crossing).

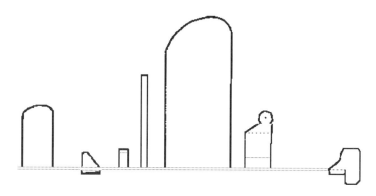

The Bleriot XI was the first aircraft to fly across the English Channel. A $2,500 prize had been offered by the London Daily Mail for the first flight across the English Channel. On July 25, 1909, Louis Bleriot collected that prize. He received orders for over a hundred Model XIs within months.

A 25 hp Anzani engine provided power in the original, though the Anzani was gradually improved, and other units used. Wingspan 25'7", length 25'.

The Bleriot XI was an extremely successful aircraft. It was built under license in many different countries.

Bleriot Model XI from Reims, France in 1909.

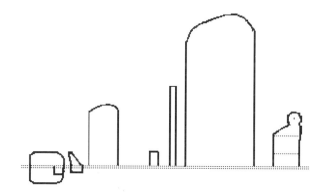

There were many single seat versions. Two-seat versions usually had slightly larger dimensions (wingspan 33'9", length 27'6", on one type).

Monoplane aircraft offered less drag, and less weight, at a time when engines and propellers were relatively heavy and inefficient.

Bleriot monoplane aircraft were known to be treacherous when pushed to their performance limits.

Build the Bleriot Model XI Monoplane

Step 1. Copy, scan and print, or trace the Bleriot TA flyer from page 4.
Note: All parts and drawings are shown in actual size throughout the book.

Step 2. Crease, then firmly bend the paper at the fold line shown below.

Step 3. Cut out the parts starting at the fold line.

Fold line $\longrightarrow$

Refer to the parts as follows:

B   e   f   g   A   d   C

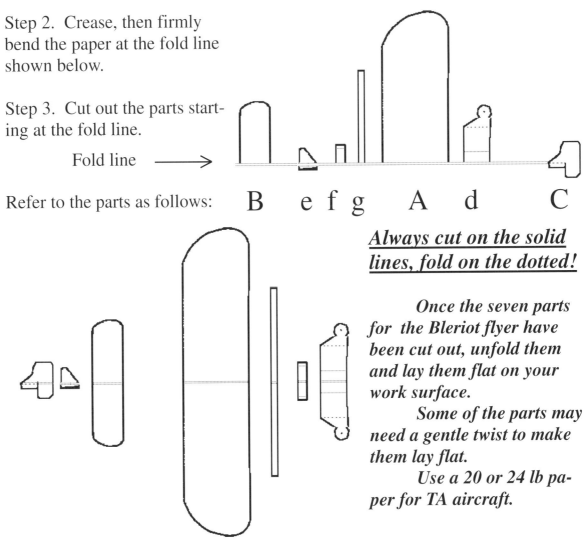

__Always cut on the solid lines, fold on the dotted!__

Once the seven parts for the Bleriot flyer have been cut out, unfold them and lay them flat on your work surface.

Some of the parts may need a gentle twist to make them lay flat.

Use a 20 or 24 lb paper for TA aircraft.

Basic Assembly

There are several options for assembling the Bleriot flyer. The simplest is to just use the wing (**A**), the tail plane (**B**), the tail fin or rudder (**C**), and a flat toothpick to create the simplest form of glider.

1. Select a straight flat toothpick, and select one side to be the top. Most flat toothpicks have a slight bevel toward the wide end, and another toward the narrow end. Make the beveled side the bottom, if present. The wide end will be the front of your aircraft, because it is slightly heavier. Place a small dab of

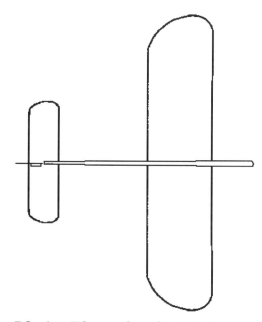

Bleriot Flyer after first 5 steps of assembly.

glue on the bottom surface, about an eighth of an inch from the small end of the tooth-pick, and carefully wipe off the excess.

Use the printed or traced side of the tail plane (and wing) as the bottom, because it will look better. Elmer's dries quickly, especially if only a light film is applied.

2. Glue the tail plane (**B**) on the bottom edge, thin end of the toothpick. Adjust the tail so that a 90 degree angle is formed to the centerline of the toothpick.

3. Place a small mark on the bottom edge of the toothpick seven-eighths of an inch from the thin end, now the back of your aircraft. This will mark for placement the rear edge of the main wing (**A**).

The printed or traced side of the wing and tail should be on the same side of your aircraft, on the bottom. Allow each new piece of your aircraft to dry.

4. Place a small smear of glue on the bottom of the toothpick, beginning at the mark, and gently press the wing (**A**) into position.

When the tail/fin rudder was cut out, a "<u>foot</u>" is formed on the fold line that will allow this part (C) to be glued to the flat surface of the tail plane.

Side view (foot)   Front view

5. Select the tail fin/rudder (**C**) and use the end of an unused toothpick to smear a small dab of glue on the forward, "foot" portion of the tail that was on the original fold line of the aircraft. At the same time adjust this "foot" so that it is at an approximate 90 degree angle to the rest of the tail. Press the foot into position on the tail plane, to the rear of the small end of the toothpick.

Adding Weight

Clip (use the nail clippers) four pieces of toothpick from the large, heavier end of an unused toothpick, each approximately five-eighths inch long. Your aircraft needs weight in front of the wing to bring the center of balance forward. Glue three pieces to the top of the toothpick, and one to the bottom. Allow them to dry. Use more weight if necessary.

Drop your aircraft from approximately 4 feet. If your aircraft glides forward, turning or even spinning, you have added enough weight.

Tuning The Bleriot XI

Building TA aircraft can be fun and rewarding, but if you don't learn to tune your aircraft, most will not fly correctly.

Look at your aircraft head on, and concentrate on the wing. The wing is usually slightly warped on a new aircraft because of the force applied to the paper when the wing is cut out. The sharper the scissors used, the less warp you will find. If the wing surface is twisted, your aircraft will spin, or at best turn to the left or right. If the tail fin is twisted, it will turn in the direction of twist.

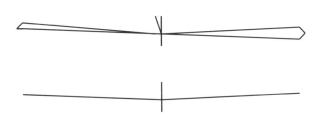

The upper head-on view shows warped, or twisted wings and tail fin/rudder. Most likely, the wings will be twisted or warped or even slightly bent when you reach this point in construction.

After the glue is dry, <u>gently</u> twist the wing in the opposite direction to the warp. The tail fin in the above drawing also represents a warp or bend that needs correction. You must look at the aircraft head on, from the front in order to see and correct these defects.

The lower head on view above shows what your aircraft should look like. Just an edge-on type view of the thin paper wing should be visible.

Reducing this twist, or warp, reduces drag, and will allow the aircraft to use the <u>lift</u> characteristics more equally for the left and right wings. The goal is <u>balance</u>, or equal lift for each wing surface.

When tuning, continuously return to the head on view to observe the twist or warp. If the wing is only slightly twisted, sometimes a simple twist in the opposite direction is all it takes.

Recognize when you have done the best tune possible. One of the effects of glue of all types on paper is warping. When the wing is glued to the tooth-pick, slight warping or ripples occur. This warping <u>can</u> cause a "camber" effect of increased lift (and drag) on one side or wing surface. If this happens, and your aircraft continues to turn to the left or right, <u>adjust the tail rudder to counter the unequal lift</u>.

Don't be to quick to give up on a TA airplane. Sometimes the very thing that gives you the most trouble can be turned to a flying advantage!

Up to this point, only the lift characteristics of a flat wing have been utilized. In "Advanced Wing Structure" we will discuss the lift advantages and disadvantages of increasing <u>camber</u>.

Finish Assembly For The Bleriot Model XI

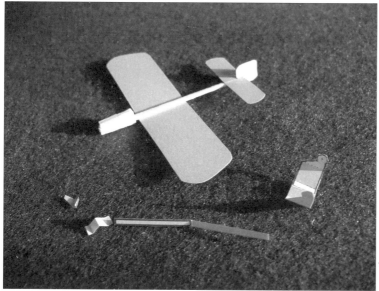

The Reim's variant of the TA Bleriot is shown with landing gear (d), tail skid (e), wing brace (f), and bracing strap (g).

Refer to page 5 for parts illustrations.

The tail skid (e) and wing brace (f) have a foot (f has two) - that is, a fold that presents a flat surface for gluing to the toothpick or wing surface.

1. The landing gear (**d**), will require special folding. When cut out, two dotted lines are visible. Bend part **d** along both dotted lines while still folded. This insures that both sides are mirror images of the other. Then reverse the fold on one side, and the landing gear should look like those in the photo above. *The drawing to the right is a frontal or head on view.*

2. Note that the lower portion of the above drawing looks a bit like a W. Place a dab of glue on the lower points of the W an eighth of an inch from the rear of the landing gear. Place a dab of glue on the rear of the tooth-pick on the underside of the front of your aircraft, just in front of the wing. Attach the landing gear by gently pressing them into place. The front of the landing gear should protrude in front of the leading edge of the wing.

3. Place a dab of glue on the "foot" of the tail skid, or part **e**. (A frontal view of part **e** will look like a capitol L. The lower portion of the L is the "foot.") Carefully press part **e** into position an eighth of an inch from the back end of the toothpick fuselage, at the rear of your aircraft.

The Reims Bleriot XI upside down, parts d and e in place.

8

4. While still folded at the original fold line, fold the wing brace (f) along the dotted line. Unfold at the center, and reverse the fold on one end of the external brace. This will create a "foot" on either side of the brace.

The Reims Bleriot XI with all seven paper parts in place.

Note the position of part f, the wing brace, and part g, the bracing strap.

Assembly of the Reims Bleriot is identical to the Bleriot that flew across the English Channel in 1909, and the Queen version.

5. Place a dab of glue on each "foot" of the wing brace (**f**) and gently position it straddling the toothpick, midway between the front and rear of the wing. Allow it to dry thoroughly.

6. Place a dab of glue on the peak of the wing brace (**f**), and lower the bracing strap (**g**) into place. It should be centered exactly on the fold line, and at a 90 degree angle to the toothpick fuselage. Allow this assembly to dry thoroughly also.

7. Place a dab of glue on the end of a toothpick, and use the toothpick to smear the glue on one end of part g, the bracing strap. Gently press the end of the bracing strap (**g**) to the wing, at the same time sliding the end toward the outer wing tip to make the strap taut. Do the same on the other side of the strap. Your aircraft is complete!

The TA Bleriot XI is an excellent glider. Practice maneuvers like turns to the left and right by (gently) warping the wings. Use the tail rudder to turn in the same direction, then try a little opposite rudder. The lift and drag created at varying speeds make the Bleriot do different and interesting maneuvers!

Tune your flyer to fly straight and practice loops. A real Model XI was the first aircraft in the world to complete a loop maneuver.

Practice landings, make your TA flyer land where and when you want it to land. A slick surface makes a good landing field. For example, if your living room is temporarily your aerodrome, spread a page from your newspaper on the carpet.

ADVANCED WING STRUCTURE

There seems still to be some controversy over just how wings provide lift. I personally have had disparaging remarks made about my lack of knowledge about lift because in a presentation I explained that a flat wing provides nearly as much lift as a cambered wing, without as much drag. The gentleman explained that he was a pilot, and that without a cambered wing a real airplane could not produce enough lift to fly. Another critic stated that the aerodynamics of flight were totally different for a toothpick sized aircraft, and that different laws applied to <u>real</u> airplanes, and real (cambered) wings.

Both of these gentlemen were partially correct, but both were wrong in the absoluteness of their arguments. My intent here is not to be controversial, but only to illustrate a point.

Wing shape (camber) causes effects that change the amount of lift a wing can generate, but the principles involved are the same no matter whether the aircraft is a modern airliner in size, or a toothpick glider. Likewise, the lift and control surfaces of toothpick sized aircraft have the <u>same functions</u> as wings, ailerons, elevators, and rudders on the real aircraft, <u>for the same reasons</u>.

A flat rigid wing (like a paper wing), large and strong enough to provide the lift necessary to get man off the ground, would be very difficult to build with today's best technology. In the Wright brothers day, it would not have been possible at all. Thus, there is a technical difference.

The fact is still the same, camber can enhance lift, but it is not required for lift. Lift is primarily a function of the angle of attack. For more discussion on how wings work, see "Why We Go Up", Robert Kunzig, DISCOVER Magazine, April 2001.

The wing cross-section below shows how chord and camber are measured.

$\longleftrightarrow$ The chord of a wing is the measure of an imaginary line stretching from the leading edge to the trailing edge.

$\updownarrow$ The camber of a wing is its measure from the top curved surface to that imaginary chord line. Most modern wings have both upper and lower camber.

The wing cross section above has under-camber. It is open on the bottom. A cambered wing produces more lift, and is stronger. In TA aircraft, flat paper wings can be made stronger, and more like the original aircraft, by adding camber. While making TA wings with no under-camber is possible, the resulting wings are heavier, tend to have worse warping problems, and can be difficult to assemble. A whole different book.

Leaving the lower surface of the wing open, however, causes a phenomenon known as under-camber. Most of the first aeroplanes were deliberately built with under-camber. Popular theory of the time held that while lift was generated by camber, increased lift or speed was possible from under-camber. For further discussion of under-camber in early aircraft, see "Undercambered Airfoils" by Caroll F. Gray, W.W.I Aero No. 170, November, 2000.

The main reason to resort to a cambered wing in TA aircraft is the increased rigidity of the paper wing. Especially in large TA aircraft, wings tend to sag as they get older. In the TA Bleriot XI the wing brace and bracing strap prevent this. An added benefit of the cambered wing for TA aircraft is realism. Many of the stability problems you will encounter will be recognizable when you read and explore accounts of the original pioneers and their aircraft flight.

HOW TO ADD CAMBER

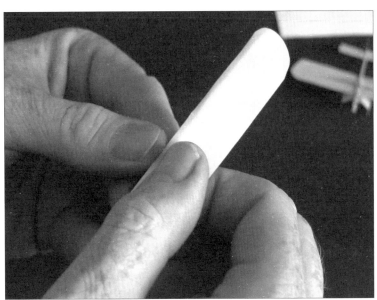

Cut out new TA Bleriot flyer parts as you did in Basic Training. Grasp the wing of your Bleriot between your thumb and fore-finger beginning at one side, about one sixteenth of an inch from the leading edge. Place the printed or traced side down or away from you, just the way it will be mounted on the aircraft. Press the leading edge of the wing down, doing the same along the entire width of the wing.

Bend the leading edge of your TA Bleriot wing down. Your airplane will be slower, glide farther.

This simple modification changes the way your TA Bleriot flies. Because of the wing's changed shape, the camber (and under camber) creates more lift and drag! Your aircraft may fly more slowly, but will probably fly farther with less thrust. Experiment by moving the cambering fold farther back on the wing, or making a second, shallower fold behind the first.

11

Bleriot Aircraft Facts

A Queen version of the Bleriot flyer was purchased by Clyde Cessna in 1911. This was his first aero plane, and he taught himself to fly over the next year. Cessna paid $7,500 dollars for the aircraft without an engine! This was his entire life's savings to that point. An Elbridge Aero Special of 40 horsepower was mounted.

Clyde Cessna went on to found the Cessna Aircraft Company.

Other famous fliers of the Bleriot were Harriet Quimby (killed flying the Bleriot), John Moisant, and Roland Garros of WWI fame.

A Swiss aviator, John Domenjoz, looped a 1914 model Bleriot XI over the Statue of Liberty. A photo of this event can be seen at the National Air & Space Museum.

A two seat version flew the first reconnaissance over German lines in WWI on August 19, 1914.

The Bleriot XI was the most commonly built monoplane in the United States prior to the 1st World War. It was manufactured under license in America by the Queen Aeroplane Company and the American Aeroplane Supply House as the Type XV.

The 1910 Gordon Bennet Trophy race was won by a 100 hp Bleriot XI flying at an average speed of 62.5 mph.

Bleriot XI built by the Queen Aeroplane Company of New York.

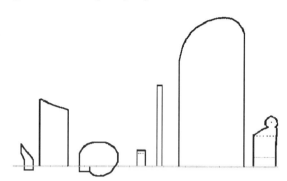

Bleriot XI 2 Seat. The fuselage for the 2 seat consists of two parts. Use instructions for Model 12 fuselage p. 65.

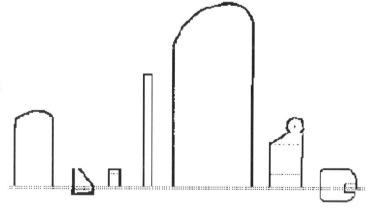

TA Experimental Airplanes

For hundreds, and perhaps thousands of years, people have been building gliders and trying to understand how birds and insects fly. Usually aircraft with engines are referred to as airplanes, and those without are referred to as gliders. Technically, gliders are airplanes! For more TA glider fun, check out "Real Glider Replicas," the first book of THE TOOTHPICK AIRFORCE series.

The glider on the left uses the longest wing, with camber. The top center glider utilizes the shortest, widest wing with no camber. It is relatively fast and maneuverable. The canard aircraft on the right utilized the medium sized wing with no camber.

The best way to determine how much weight you need is to drop your airplane about four feet above the floor. Continue to add weight until the airplane glides forward, even if it turns or spins. Add weight by cutting and gluing tooth-pick blocks to the fuselage in front of the wing.

The jets below need less weight, but need extreme tuning and patience.

The aircraft to the left were constructed from the TA Block Glider pattern on the opposite page. Construction is very similar to the instruction found in Basic Training With the Bleriot Model XI. Unless directed otherwise, always begin assembling your aircraft with the tail. This will resolve in part how far forward to place the wing. When I design my own aircraft I need to put enough space between the tail and wing to fit my thumb and forefinger, for launching purposes.

The left glider has two camber folds, while the flying wing on the right has no tail plane!

Although a balance point does exist in most gliders close to mid-wing, the more reliable way to add weight to your airplane is by actually testing its glide as described above.

13

EXPERIMENTAL GLIDER AIRPLANES

While building and flying experimental gliders may not be physically essential to the construction of the historical replicas in this book, understanding the basics of flight is essential to making them fly. As Wilbur Wright said, "It is possible to fly without motors, but not without knowledge and skill."

The TA Block Glider at the right allows experimentation with ailerons, wing lengths and alternative tails.

The photo on page 13 shows several variations, including one with the tail-plane placed forward of the wing. This makes a very effective glider, and works similarly to the biplane gliders and airplanes the Wright brothers built. These gliders are also perfect for experimenting with camber and under-camber. Try building the flying wing!

TA Block Glider w/Ailerons

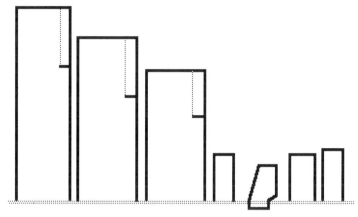

TA Rounded Wingtip Glider w/ailerons.

Both of the gliders on this page have movable wing control surfaces. The Round Wingtip Glider adds movable elevators. They fly indoors or out, but pick a calm, dry day for outdoor flying.

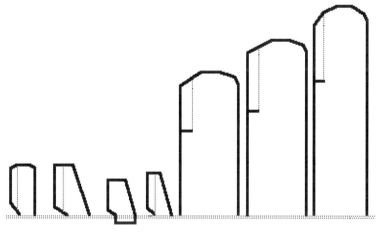

The drawings on this page may be copied or scanned and printed with the author and BOOGER RED'S BOOKS INC. permission for the express and sole purpose of building TA aircraft.

TA Experimental Swept Wing Glider with alternative wing, tail planes and rudders. Swept wings reduce drag, but produce lift on a longer axis!

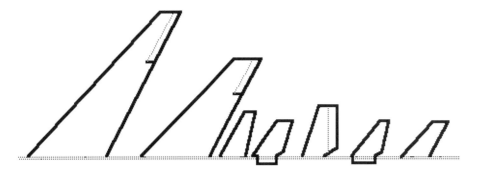

TA Ex. Alternative Lift Wings. Learn the concepts, design your own wings!

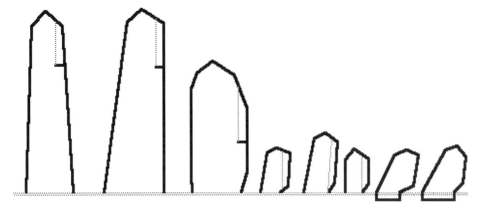

The drawings on this page may be copied or scanned and printed with the author and BOOGER RED'S BOOKS INC. permission for the express and sole purpose of building TA aircraft.

Building The Wright Flyers

The 1902 Wright glider was the first aircraft ever that had control over all three axes: yaw, pitch and roll. A single tail rudder controlled yaw, or right and left turns. This glider was first built with a double, non-steering rudder. The Wrights made almost 1,000 glides with this aircraft during September and October of 1902. When the change was made to a single, steer-able rudder, their glide times increased.

Wright 1902 glider with single tail rudder.

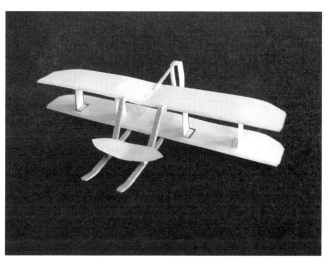

The TA Wright 1902 Glider w/double tail.

The Wrights called the elevator, which they placed in front of the main wings, a horizontal rudder. This "horizontal rudder" provided control over the pitch of their airplane. In other words they were able to make their airplane go up and down by working a lever.

Wilbur Wright discovered wing warping when he was able to visualize the top and bottom surfaces of a bicycle inner tube box as wing surfaces. When one end of the box was twisted down, the other end was twisted up. In this motion, Wilbur could envision the flight of birds and the way their wings worked. The bi-plane design provided the lift, and was strong enough to make the wing warping work. This wing warping system was incorporated into Wright designs up to World War I, and Wright airplanes were known as the safest airplanes of the early times.

The Wright 1902 glider had a 32 foot wingspan and was 16.1 feet long. It only weighed 112 pounds. The Wrights continued using this glider in 1903, while they worked on the powered flyer. When the single rudder was replaced with a double, steering rudder, they were able to glide for 43 seconds.

The TA 1902 glider copies the biplane design of the original, and introduces several new airplane building skills you will need to complete all THE TOOTHPICK AIRFORCE replicas you will find in The First Flyers.

The Wrights developed biplane type aircraft, or airplanes with two main wings, one above the other. Other pioneers, mainly European, developed monoplanes, or airplanes with only one wing.

Building a biplane is more complicated than building a monoplane. However there were advantages in lift and strength upon which the Wrights were able to capitalize. The same advantages and disadvantages apply to TA biplanes.

Wright 1902 Glider.

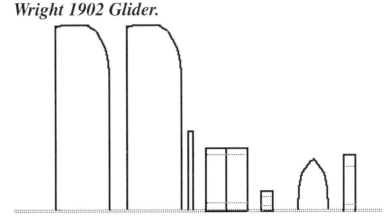

Wright Kitty Hawk Flyer of 1903.

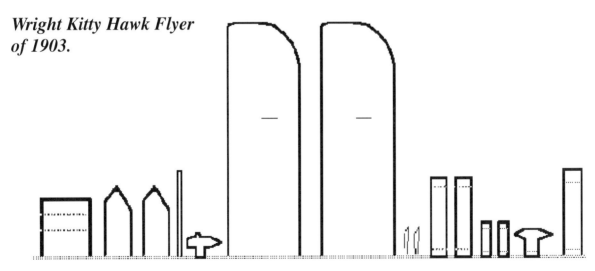

TA Wright 1902 Glider

Step 1. Copy, scan and print, or trace the TA Wright 1902 Glider on the previous page.

Step 2. Crease, then firmly bend the paper at the fold line shown below.

Step 3. Cut out the parts starting at the fold line.

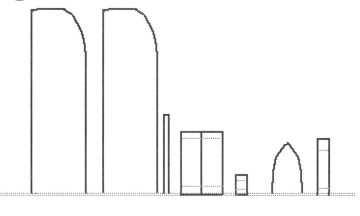

A B G C$_{1-4}$ D$_{1,2}$ E F

Refer to the parts as labeled above:

Before separating (cutting) the wing struts (C), fold the struts along the fold lines, to make "feet" on either end. All four struts should have an identical "foot" on both ends as shown: ⟶

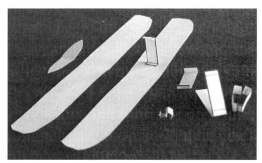

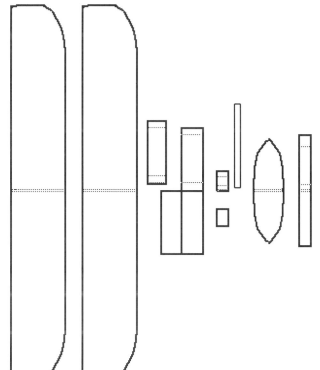

Wright 1902 Glider with folds made on one pair of struts, the tail assembly, and the elevator struts.

  The drawing to the left shows the 12 paper parts to the TA Wright 1902 ready for assembly.

  1. Parts **A**, **B** (wings), and **C** (4 wing struts), make up the wing assembly. Make the folds along the dotted lines while each pair of struts is still connected at the base, or original fold line. Make the fold away from the base first, and crease it firmly. When both folds have been made, cut the struts apart on the original fold line.

18

Prepare your wings, placing the printed side down. If you wish to add camber to the wing, follow the instructions now in "How to Add Camber."

The struts (parts **C1-4**) should be placed midway (or slightly forward) between the leading edge and the trailing edge of the wing. A pencil mark on the wing where you intend to glue the strut is a good idea.

Dab glue on one foot of the first strut, and gently press it into position one half inch from the center line (the original fold line) on what is now designated as the lower wing.

Glue the second strut into position to match the first, on the other side of the lower wing. Glue the remaining struts into place a half inch from the outer tip of the lower wing.

Make sure each foot has a 90 degree fold that makes it perpendicular to the strut. Each foot should provide a flat surface to attach the upper wing.

Place the upper wing (printed side up) on your work area, then dab glue on the ends of the "feet" on the lower wing.

Carefully position the lower wing directly above the upper wing, and press it into place.

Allow the assembly to dry.

The wing assembly, with the "feet" positioned above the upper wing. Also shown are the elevator with folded struts, and the tail assembly glued "closed."

2. The elevator struts (parts **D1,2**) should be bent along the fold lines to form feet, then set aside.

3. To assemble your TA Wright 1902 Glider with a single tail, cut the second tail off at the original fold line. Trim off the excess at the end of the upper "foot." Recommended: Build your first TA Wright Glider with the double tail, because it is stronger.

To assemble the double tail, make the bends at the dotted lines on part **F**, starting at the upper end, away from the original fold line. Reverse the folds on one side, to form a box, as shown in the photo above. Make the top end the same width as the bottom, and glue the top end of the tail structure closed. The tail assembly top strap (**G**) will be used to connect the upper wing to the tail assembly in the step 2 on the next pages. Set it aside for now.

For the final assembly of the TA Wright 1902 Glider select two similar flat toothpicks. Not all toothpicks have <u>similar straightness, width, and thickness</u>. Choose carefully because your aircraft will look and fly better.

Most flat toothpicks are about two and one-fourth inches long. Clip five-eighths of an inch from the small, slender end of each toothpick. Both should now measure one and five-eighths in length. Save both parts of the toothpicks.

For the next step, you must learn to <u>bend</u> toothpicks. Grasp the flat, wider end of one of the toothpicks, and bend it as close to one quarter of an inch from the end as possible. When you hear and feel it crack, stop! We want the bent end to stay attached. We are building landing skids for your glider.

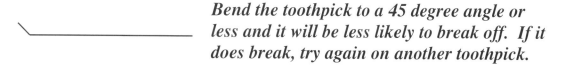

Bend the toothpick to a 45 degree angle or less and it will be less likely to break off. If it does break, try again on another toothpick.

Bend the second toothpick to match, and smear glue on the top, bottom, and sides of both at the bend. The glue is to seal and strengthen the bend.

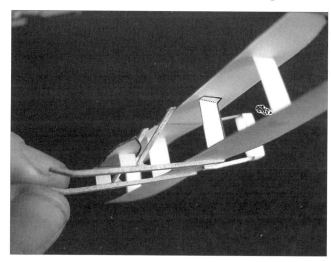

Fully assembled glider shows toothpick frame attachment to wing, elevator and elevator strut attachment, and tail assembly attachment. Refer back to this photo.

Step 1. Place the wing assembly upside down on your work surface. Make a small mark in pencil one quarter of an inch on one side, and then the other side of the center (original fold) line.

Using a <u>small</u> amount of glue, smear the top rear (small end) surface of one of the toothpicks, and press it into place, starting one-sixteenth of an inch from the trailing edge of the wing, on your mark. The toothpick should protrude in front of your wing at a 90 degree angle. Glue the second skid in place on the other side.

Step 2. Grasp one of the five-eighth inch pieces of toothpick that was clipped off for the skids, and "bend" it up one-eighth of an inch from the large end.

The tail rudder support has two bends, one up, the rear down.

Bend it down at the rear, small end of the toothpick. This is the tail rudder support, and it raises the tail rudder a fraction of an inch.

After the landing skids have dried, place the wing and skid assembly upside down on your work surface. Smear a dab of glue on the large end of the tail rudder support, in front of the one-eighth inch bend. Glue the bent end of the tail rudder support to the rear (trailing) edge of your wing, on the center line, so that bend is away from you (down). The tail rudder support should protrude from the rear of your aircraft at a 90 degree angle, parallel to, but behind and between the landing skids. Allow this structure to dry.

Dab glue on the last one-eighth inch of the toothpick tail rudder support and carefully place the rudder assembly (**F**) into position. The rudder assembly will hang, and gravity will hold it in position once it is turned with one open end facing the front. Allow to dry.

Turn the glider assembly right side up. Use a toothpick to smear glue on rear (one quarter inch) of the fold line at the trailing edge of the top wing. Gently press the tail assembly top strap (**G**) so that the end is centered on the top of the tail rudder (**F**) assembly. Use the toothpick to smear glue on the

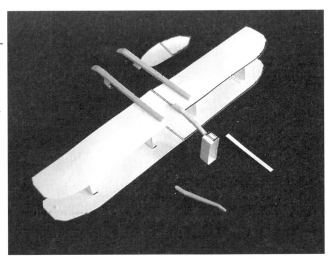

Wing assembly with tail rudder support in place, and rudder assembly hanging in position. Note the <u>extra</u> toothpick rudder support with the proper bends. Landing skids have elevator struts attached.

rear of the strap, then press it in place on the top of the tail rudder assembly. Refer to the photo on the previous page if necessary for placement.

Step 3. Place a dab of glue one-half inch forward of the wing on the upper side of each landing skid, and press the elevator struts (**D**) into place, parallel with the landing skid. When these are dry, dab glue on the top "foot" of each elevator strut, and gently press the elevator in position. Center the elevator using the original fold line, placing the rear (trailing) edge of the elevator three-eighths of an inch from the forward edge of the lower wing. Allow to dry.

The final step of construction is the forward airframe. This part of the TA Wright 1902 Glider serves as an important part of the airframe, providing strength and rigidity, and a good portion of the weight necessary to make this glider soar. Most TA gliders have a toothpick nose that extends out further than the nose of the aircraft being modeled. This is necessary for balance.

Step 4. Clip the rounded tip from two toothpicks of similar size to make a flatter gluing surface. Place glue (generously when connecting toothpick to toothpick) on the wide (now flat) end, then dab glue on the forward edge of the upper wing directly above the landing skid. Lean the toothpick against the upper wing (on the glue), and press the wide end against the upper landing skid just behind the elevator. Repeat the process for the toothpick on the other side. Let it dry.

Toothpicks for upper airframe glued in place provide weight for balance.

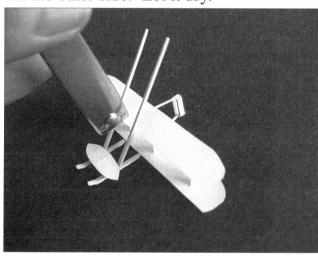

Bigger, sharper clippers are better!

Clip the upper ends off the airframe toothpicks even with the top of the wing. If one side comes loose, just re-glue it and set it aside to dry.

Tuning The Bi-plane

Bi-planes such as the TA Wright 1902 Glider should be tuned in the same way as the Bleriot and others in the basic training section.

Look at your glider from a head on view, concentrating on the wings. There will be some warping where the struts are attached, and this needs to be corrected, if possible. Bend or twist the wings carefully, to balance the lift.

Launch the TA glider with a grip on one of the toothpick skids. If your glider dives and won't pull out, add some "up" elevator.

Clip both toothpicks off even with the top of the wing.

22

The First Powered Flight

On December 17, 1903, the Wright brothers made four flights with their first powered flyer at Kitty Hawk, North Carolina. Orville flew about 120 feet and stayed aloft about 12 seconds. Wilbur managed to fly 852 feet and stayed in the air for 59 seconds.

The Wright brothers had to teach themselves to fly in brief seconds, in an airplane with controls and control surfaces that were barely adequate.

The Kitty Hawk flyer had a 40 foot 4 inch wingspan and was only a little over 21 feet long. It weighed only 605 lbs. The Kitty Hawk flyer had twin tail rudders, and a 15 or 16 horsepower engine.

Although the first to actually fly, the Kitty Hawk flyer only made four flights. It was damaged by wind after the fourth flight, and the Wrights packed it up and shipped it back to Dayton, Ohio. Its flying days were over.

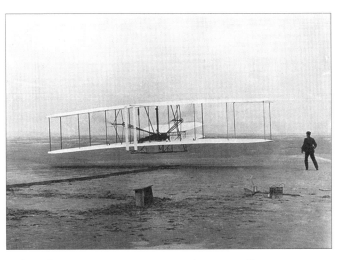

The dream comes true. Powered, controlled flight became reality on December 17, 1903 at Kitty Hawk, North Carolina.

TA Wright Kitty Hawk Flyer.

The TA Kitty Hawk Flyer is (approximately) scaled to the TA Wright 1902 Glider, the Bleriot Model XI, and the rest of the aircraft in this book. Scaling the first flyers is very difficult because while some aircraft dimensions are known, many have dimensions that vary according to the source. As with most TA airplanes, the need for balance and the use of toothpick airframes makes these airplanes a little longer in the front than the original.

TA biplanes take more effort and concentration in tuning to make them fly, but do glide beautifully. Where else can you see and fly Wright airplanes?

TA Wright Kitty Hawk Flyer

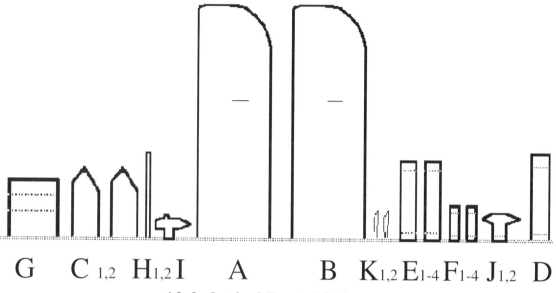

G   C 1,2   H1,2 I   A   B   K1,2 E1-4 F1-4 J1,2 D

Alphabetical Parts Listing:

A and B are the main wings.
C 1,2 are the elevators.
D is the tail assembly.
E 1-4 are the main wing struts.
F 1-4 are the elevator struts.

G is the landing skid frame.
H 1,2 are the tail assembly top straps.
I is the motor.
J 1,2 are propeller mounts.
K 1,2 are propellers.

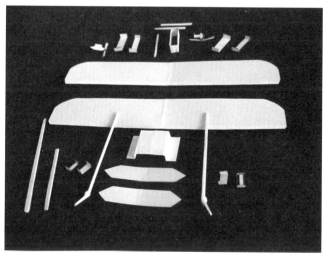

Parts shown ready to assemble. Landing skids bent, with glue applied to bends, struts folded, tail rudders glued, propeller assemblies complete.

Step 1. Copy, scan and print, or trace the TA Wright Kitty Hawk Flyer on page 17.

Step 2. Crease, then firmly bend the paper at the fold line.

Step 4. Cut out the parts starting at the fold line.

Step 5. Make the additional bends for (feet) struts, motor, propeller mounts, landing skid frame, and tail parts ***before*** unfolding at original fold line!

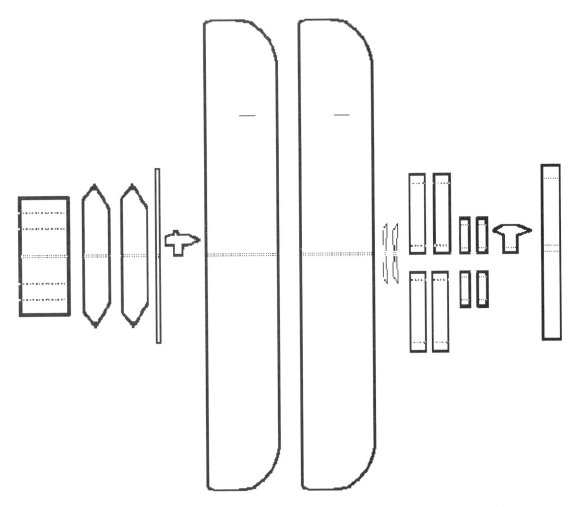

TA Kitty Hawk Flyer with 21 parts cut out. This glider may fly a little "cleaner" by leaving off parts I, J1&2, K1,2. These detail parts are optional, simply skip these assembly steps.

TA Kitty Hawk Flyer bottom & rear view.

The TA Kitty Hawk Flyer with engine, propeller mounts, and propellers is an excellent glider, or simplify it by leaving these parts off!

The TA Kitty Hawk Flyer to the left has a cambered wing, a single bend running the width of the entire wing about one-sixteenth of an inch from the front edge. Add weight by gluing three-eighths inch blocks of toothpick in front of the elevator, on top of the landing

Assemble the TA Kitty Hawk Flyer

If you wish to add the optional engine, propellers, and propeller assemblies begin with Special Assembly, below. The TA Kitty Hawk Flyer flies a little better and is easier to build without these parts. Instructions in this book assume that you have completed the construction of prior gliders and grasp the concepts, for example, the "feet" on the wing struts in the photo below.

Special Assembly: Fold the propeller mounts (**I**) on the fold line to make a "foot" for each propeller mount. Cut the propeller mounts apart now. Unfold the propellers (**K**), and glue one each to the longer end of each propeller mount. Fold the engine mount "foot." Set these parts aside to dry.
Step 1. Select one wing (**A** or **B**), to be the bottom wing. This will be wing assembly "**A**" when we begin construction. Likewise, assembly "**B**" will consist of the top wing.

If you wish to add camber

Bottom wing assembly is shown (at top), just below tail assembly. Top wing assembly (B) has struts and propellers.

follow the instructions in "How to Add Camber" (p.11) now.

Place wing **A** upside down on your work surface.

Select the landing skid frame (**G**) and make the two folds along the dotted lines starting at the outside (away from the original fold line). Unfold part (**G**) on the original fold line, so that it will lay flat. With the printed side up, reverse the fold on the outside of the printed side. Now reverse the inside fold on the unprinted side of the landing skid frame.

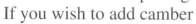 *Viewed from the front, part G should look like this.*

Dab glue thinly along the fold line in the center, and the outside edges of part **G** (on the bottom as viewed above) and press it in place on the bottom of Wing **A**. The original fold line on the bottom of part **G** should be lined up with the original fold line on Wing **A**, one-eighth of an inch from the leading edge of the wing. While Wing assembly **A** dries, prepare wing assembly **B**.

Place wing **B** upside down on your work surface. Dab glue on one end of the feet of the wing struts (**E1-4**), and glue them into position. The inside struts should be one-half inch from the center "original" fold line, while the outside struts should be one and one-half inches from the center line. If you intend to mount the propellers, place a dab of glue on the "foot" of each propeller mount and glue each one three-fourths of an inch from the center line, with the rear edge of the foot even with the trailing edge of the wing. Wing assembly **B** is now ready for assembly, when the glue is dry.

Bend two toothpicks, of similar shape and weight, one-quarter of an inch from the larger, wider end, to a 45 degree angle. Smear glue on the bend on both sides, top and bottom, and allow to dry. Using the clippers, snip seven-eighths of an inch from the small, narrow end of a toothpick. This will be the tail rudder support. Save the rest of the toothpick, it will form half of the forward air frame.

Smear glue on one of the toothpick landing skids, and glue it into place on the extended "foot" formed by the outside fold of the landing skid frame. Now glue the second skid into place, making them parallel to each other. Each skid should protrude to the rear of the wing one-eighth inch, and behind the landing skid frame (approximately) five-eighths inch. Refer to the photo on the previous page, and below. Note that the toothpick skids are at a 90 degree angle to the wing assembly **A.** Smear glue on the thicker end of the tail rudder support and glue it into position on the centerline at the trailing edge of the **A** wing assembly. All but one-eighth inch of the tail rudder support should protrude to the rear of the **A** wing assembly. Allow assembly to dry.

Special assembly: smear glue on the engine (**I**) "foot", and glue it in place one-eight of an inch to the right of the centerline on the top surface of wing assembly A. The front of the engine should be one-eighth inch behind the

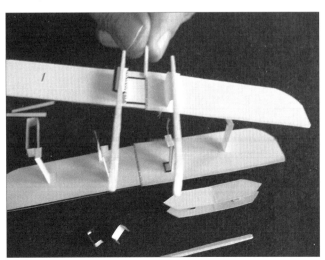

Smear glue on the struts, line the bottom wing A up with B, and press in place.

forward edge of the wing (A).

Step 2. Smear glue on the wing struts bottom feet (the wing assembly, **B**, should be lying upside-down still). Carefully line up wing assembly **A** so that it is directly above **B**, and lower it into place. Allow this assembly to dry.

Place one elevator (**C**) upside down on your workspace (print side up).

27

Smear glue on one end of two elevator struts (part **F 1-4**), and glue them into position three-eighths of an inch from the centerline of the elevator. This is now your top elevator. Smear glue on the bottom end of the same elevator struts, and press the top elevator in place. Make sure that the print side is up, as you are looking at the bottom of your elevator assembly. Allow this assembly to dry.

Fold the tail assembly (**D**) into a rectangular box by reversing the folds on one side of the assembly. Refer to the photos on page 26 and below. Place the wing assembly upside down on your work surface, and hang the tail assembly on the tail rudder support, centering the original fold line on the end of the toothpick support. Align the tail assembly carefully as these are the glider's twin rudders. Allow this assembly a couple minutes to dry, upside down.

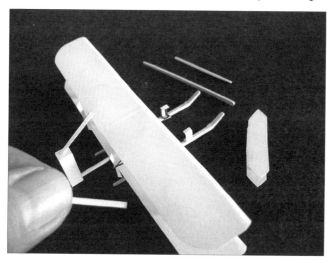

Carefully press the tail assembly top straps into position above the small end of the landing skids.

Smear glue on the bottom "feet" of the remaining two elevator struts (F1-4) and press them in place on the top surface of the landing skids, one half-inch in front of the leading edge of the lower wing. While they dry…

Dab glue on one end of the tail assembly top straps (**H1,2**), and press them (gently) in place on the top wing, directly above the ends of the landing skids. Line up the other end over the tail assembly.

Dab glue on the elevator struts, and press the elevator assembly in place, centering it using the original fold line.

Now dab glue on the tail assembly straps and press them into place on the top of the tail rudder assembly (**D**).

Clip the rounded ends from the large end of two toothpicks. Use the piece from the tail.

Airframe glued into position.

Dab glue on the wider end of the toothpick air frame, and press it on the landing skid just behind the elevator assembly. Dab glue on the wing directly above the landing skid, and press the toothpick against the wing, while maintaining its position on the landing skid. Refer to the photo on page 28. Do the same to the toothpick airframe on the other side, and allow them to dry.

Clip the ends off the toothpick airframe where it protrudes above the wing. If the glue comes loose from the wing, or the landing skid below, re-glue, using plenty of glue for this application only. Allow the TA Kitty Hawk Flyer to dry before tuning.

Line up the blades of the clippers so that they strike squarely on the toothpick, just above the wing.

Final walk around on your new TA Kitty Hawk Flyer: Additional glue can be added to strengthen the connecting point between the airframe base and the landing skid on each side. If additional weight is necessary in tuning, add one-quarter to three-eighth inch toothpick blocks in front of the elevator, on top of the landing skids. If up elevator is needed,

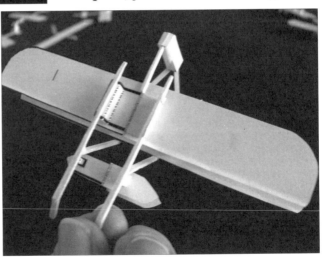

bend the leading edges upward, and the entire structure (gently) to the rear.

Step 3. Tune the TA Kitty Hawk Flyer by first examining the wings from the head on view. Gently adjust by twisting or bending the wing surfaces to provide equal lift on each side. There will be some warping from the area the struts attach to, due to the warping caused by gluing the two surfaces together.

Adjust the elevators to provide a slight lift, and glide the aircraft by grasping one of the toothpick landing skids. More weight will probably be required. Add weight in short lengths of toothpick, glued to the upper surface of the forward landing skids.

When the TA Flyer glides 20 to 30 feet with a small thrust, she is tuned.

Wright 1905 Flyer III

The original Wright 1905 Flyer III first flew on June 23rd, 1905. Like the 1904 Flyer II, Flyer III had pitch control problems (the elevator controlled the angle of attack of the wing, or pitch.) There was a separate problem in making turns. The first Flyer III was not stable enough to be a reliable flyer.

1904 had been a busy year for the Wright brothers. They moved their flying operations to Huffman Prairie, outside of Dayton, Ohio. At Huffman Prairie the Wrights did not have the steady winds that had made Kitty Hawk so attractive for their gliding and first flights. This lack of prevailing winds created an immediate problem in launching their airplane. (The Wrights, and most of the pioneers used the term aeroplane. In fact, the term aeroplane is still commonly used in Europe.)

To deal with the lack of wind the Wrights constructed a wooden derrick with which they hoisted, then dropped a twelve to fourteen hundred pound weight. The weight pulled a rope through a system of pulleys on the launching rail, back to a trolley upon which the flyer was mounted. When the weight dropped, the flyer was pulled down the launching rail. The Wrights used this launching method for all of their airplanes until early 1910, when they began using wheels for takeoff and landing.

The Wright Flyer II was built and flown in 1904 between May and December. The Wright brothers made one hundred and five flights at Huffman Prairie in this aircraft. However, their best two flights were of only five minutes duration, and while this still was the longest flying time in the world at the time, the Wrights recognized that control was still a problem.

The Flyer II, III (background), Model A, and 1909 Military Flyers used a catapult and launching track for takeoff until early 1910. (Photo of model at Smithsonian.)

The Flyer II was of the same dimensions as the Kitty Hawk Flyer, but had weights attached to the front elevator in an attempt to improve stability.

When the Flyer III was rebuilt after a severe crash in July 1905, the brothers moved the elevator assembly twice as far forward, and the tail farther back from the wing. They also made the rudder control separate from the wing warping controls. With the changes, Wilbur flew 39.5 minutes, longer than

all their previous flight times totaled together. The
newly rebuilt Flyer III provided the stability and controlled flight that the Wrights were searching for. The
brothers continued to make longer and better flights
for another month, then disassembled their Flyer III
and packed it away. Another problem remained: how
to market the worlds first practical airplane.

Wright Flyer III.

It would be two and one-half years, May of
1908, before the Wrights flew again.

Even though all of their 1904 and 1905 flights were conducted in view of
the public, there were many who doubted the Wright brothers' claims. In par-
ticular the US government and military offices the Wrights contacted were
skeptical. The brothers tried to interest foreign governments, the French and
the British, only after being rejected by their own.

In 1907 the Wright brothers packed a new airplane they had modified
from the 1905 Flyer III, and sailed to France. Their attempts to interest the
French failed at that time, but they left their airplane packed for shipping in
France, and returned home.

In 1908 the Wrights finally received what they considered fair offers
from the French, as well as the U.S. government.

The Wrights hurriedly
shipped their 1905 Flyer III to
Kitty Hawk where they made substantial modifications. They
added two seats to carry a passenger, and a more powerful engine
of 30 horsepower replaced the 20
horsepower unit. The controls
were changed to levers because
the pilot would no longer be lying
prone on the wing in a harness.

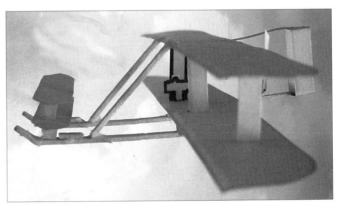

*THE TOOTHPICK AIRFORCE version
of the Wright Flyer III. The real (and the
TA) Wright Flyer III had a larger tail and
elevators than the Kitty Hawk Flyer. More
significant was the increased distance between the elevators and the wings.*

The changes were made
satisfactorily, and Wilbur took up
the first passenger in the history
of heavier-than-air flight. Both
brothers flew until Wilbur experi-
enced a flying accident on May
14, 1908. Although Wright walked away, Flyer III was not repaired.

1905 Wright Flyer III

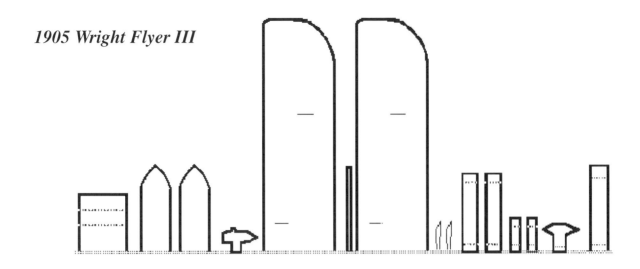

Wright 1908 Model A

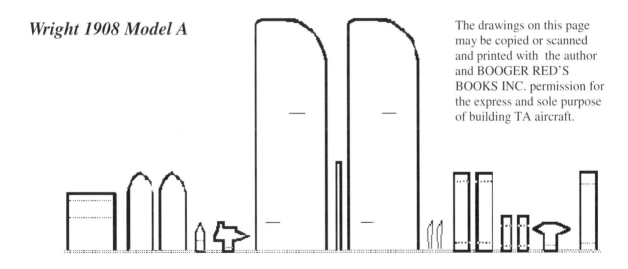

TA Wright Flyer III

G C 1,2   I   A H   B K1,2E1-4 F1-4 J1,2 D

Alphabetical Parts Listing:

A and B are the main wings.
C 1,2 are the elevators.
D is the tail assembly.
E 1-4 are the main wing struts.
F 1-4 are the elevator struts.

G is the landing skid frame.
H is the tail assembly top strap.
I is the motor.
J 1,2 are propeller mounts.
K 1,2 are propellers.

Step 1. Copy, scan and print, or trace the TA Wright Flyer III on the previous page.
Step 2. Crease, then firmly bend the paper at the fold line.
Step 3. Cut out the parts starting at the fold line.
Step 4. Make all the folds on the dotted lines for each part. Start at the fold farthest away from the original fold line. Reverse the necessary folds for the tail assembly (**D**) and landing skid frame (**G**).
Step 5. Bend landing skids at 45 degrees, three-eighths of an inch from the wide, front end. Smear

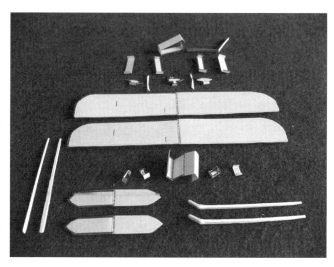

All parts shown ready for assembly.

glue on the top and bottom of the bend on the landing skids, to seal and strengthen.

TA 1905 Wright Flyer III

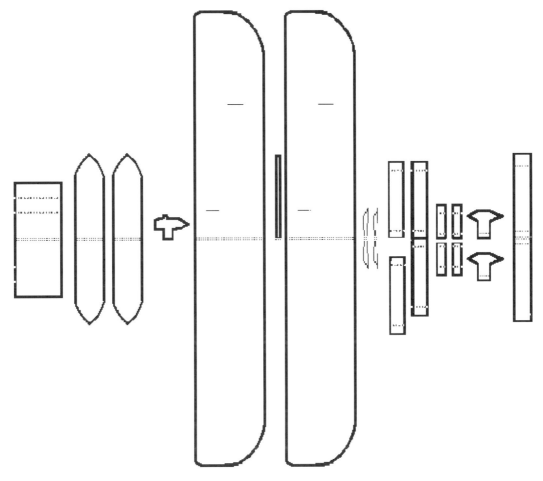

Parts shown above are cut out and shown laid out flat only for identification. Make all the necessary folds to struts, tail, propellers and mounts, and landing skid frame along the dotted lines <u>before</u> unfolding from original fold line.

Warning! Previous construction techniques and skills should be followed from this point forward. Specific instruction will be detailed only for new or different assemblies. Refer back to assembly of previous airplanes for skill and technique review.

Longer airframe toothpicks mean less weight will have to be added when tuning Flyer III.

Add camber to the upper and lower wings before beginning assembly. See page 11 for more detail. Adding camber is recommended for this glider.

Step 1. Glue the tail assembly (**D**) together at the top, making the rectangular box shape shown in the photo.

Glue the propellers (**K1,2**) in place on the propeller mounts (**J1,2**).

Glue the wing struts (**E1-4**) to the upper wing (**B**), with the inside pair one-half inch from centerline, the outside struts one and one-half inches from the center, original fold line.

Always allow glue to dry.

Instruction steps at the left are shown proceeding from top to bottom above.

Glue the landing skid frame (**G**) in place, lining up the center fold line with the wing center, one-eighth of an inch from the leading edge of the wing.

Glue two elevator struts (**F1-4**) three-eighths of an inch to either side of the centerline of the upper elevator.

Step 2. Glue the propeller assemblies (**K+J**) in place three-fourths of an inch from the centerline of the upper wing (**B**), on the trailing edge.

Glue the toothpick landing skids in place on the landing skid frame (**G**) at a 90 degree angle to the bottom wing assembly (**A**), one eighth inch protruding to the rear.

Cut one and one-eighth inches off the narrow end of a toothpick for a tail assembly support. Glue the toothpick tail assembly support to the bottom wing (**A**) on the centerline. One inch should protrude to the rear.

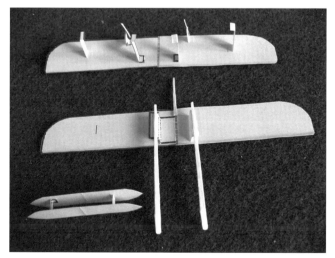

Step 2 instructions are illustrated in the above photograph, top to bottom.

Place glue on the "feet" of the elevator struts (**F**), and glue the bottom, lower elevator (**C**) in place.

Step 3.

Glue engine one-fourth inch to the left of center (head on view).

Straighten the wing struts (**E1-4**) so that they stand up from the upper wing assembly (**B**) at a 90 degree angle. Place glue on the wing struts "feet" and carefully lower the lower wing assembly into position. One wing should be directly above the other.

Hang the tail assembly (**D**) on the tail assembly support, adjusting the tail rudders carefully.

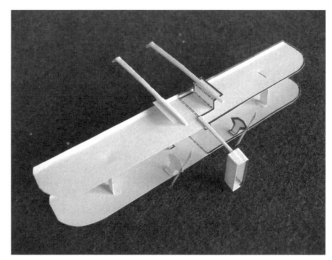

Fold the propeller assemblies flat on the wing to lay the top wing assembly (B) upside down on your work surface.

The toothpick airframe completes Flyer III's airframe, strengthening the whole assembly. Glue the rear airframe parts on the upper wing directly above skids.

Step 4. Glue the remaining elevator struts (**F**) in place just behind the 45 degree bend of the toothpick landing skids.

Glue the tail assembly top strap (**H**) to the top wing, aligning it over the tail assembly (**D**).

Glue one side of a toothpick airframe (an unused toothpick) to the toothpick landing skid, and dab glue on the upper wing directly above the landing skid. The bottom of the airframe should be placed forward seven-eighths inch in front of the wing. Allow this assembly to dry.

Step 5. Clip the portion of the toothpick airframes off that protrudes above the wing. Re-glue if necessary, using plenty of glue at the junction of the landing skids and the toothpick airframes.

Place glue on the elevator feet, and lower the elevator assembly in position, centering and aligning it at 90 degrees to the skids.

Glue the tail assembly top strap to the tail assembly.

Tune the TA Flyer III in the same manner as the Kitty Hawk flyer, page 29. A couple extra one-fourth inch toothpick blocks may increase the glide.

1908 Wright Model A Flyer

On December 27, 1907 the U.S. War Department, through the Signal Corps, issued an "Advertisement and Specification for a Heavier-Than-Air Flying Machine" that was capable of carrying two men at a speed of 40 miles an hour and of staying in the air for at least one hour and landing without serious damage. The War Department was required to accept bids for its first flyer.

The *American Magazine of Aeronautics* printed this response to this requirement: "There is not a known flying-machine in the world which could fulfill these specifications." The world still doubted the Wrights' success.

To discourage charlatans, bidders were required to deposit with the Signal Corps a certified check amounting to 10 percent of the bid, to be forfeited in case of failure. Although the Wrights were not the lowest bidder, the War Department accepted two bids. This meant that the cash-strapped War Department would have to pay for two machines if both were successful in trials.

Augustus M. Herring, who had many claims and few successes in flight, was the only other bidder. He never met the War Department requirements.

The Wright brothers were able to meet the challenge of the War Department, and a separate bid in France. In March 1908, a French syndicate made an offer to form a company to build Wright airplanes. The company, "La Compagnie Generale de Navigation Aerienne," would be capitalized at 700,000 francs, or 140,000 dollars. The Wrights would receive most of the company stock, royalties on all machines constructed, and a substantial sum in cash. All this depended on the successful demonstration of their airplane in France. The requirements of this demonstration were two flights of at least 50 kilometers within an hour or less.

There was no competition from French fliers. There was no airplane in the world that could be reliably launched, flown and landed, then re-launched and flown those distances other than the Wright's.

Likewise, in America, no airplane other than the Wright Model A could have carried a passenger aloft for over an hour to meet the Signal Corps requirements. The Wright brothers now had the contracts they had wanted for two and one-half years, although they had not flown for all that time. They had, however, constructed a pair of the airplanes that

Model A in flight.

would be known as Wright Model A Flyers. One was in storage in France, the other was being readied for their U.S. Army trials at Fort Myer, Virginia.

On August 8, 1908, Wilbur Wright was able to make his first flight in the Model A Flyer at an automobile racetrack near Le Mans, France. Although skeptical, the French public and press showed up in numbers. Four members of the Aero-Club De France were present, led by Ernest Archdeacon. Louis Bleriot, who had just built and completed his eighth and most successful airplane, was also there.

Wilbur was dressed in a gray business suit and wore his usual high starched collar. He worked and made adjustments to the Model A until his audience was quite frustrated. But Wright knew this had to be a successful flight, and wanted to impress his audience with success, not failure.

Finally, at 6:30 p.m., Wright started the engine, turned his cap with the bill to the rear, and had the weights released in the starting derrick. The Model A seemed to leap into the air when compared with the long takeoff runs for the French flyers of the time, and caused a panic when it headed for a stand of poplar trees. The French airplanes of the time required large open areas, because turns were made only more or less successfully, and not always predictably.

Wright banked sharply, turned his airplane short of the trees and swept around the racetrack oval, making sharp turns the French thought impossible. After two laps of the race course he brought the Model A in for a smooth landing only 50 feet from the starting rail. The French were wild with their praise. One member of the French Aero-Club told a reporter, "Mr. Wright has us all in his hands." Another witness stated the Model A "is wonderful, we are as children compared to the Wrights." Louis Bleriot, one of France's most successful aviators, said "A new era in mechanical flight has commenced."

The press summed up their reaction in the Sunday *Le Figaro,* stating Wright's "flight was not a success, but a triumph, a decisive victory that amounted to a revolution in the scientific world."

Wilbur Wright spent 6 months flying, carrying passengers, and not only successfully completed the trials, but trained pilots for the Wrights' new aircraft factory in France.

Orville Wright was busy on the other side of the Atlantic, at Ft. Myer, Virginia. On September 3, 1908, he made a flight of just over a minute. His flights grew longer as he practiced with the new controls. Remember, the Model A was a new machine, and had never been flown. On September 8th Orville made a world record flight of 57 and one-half minutes. Where Curtiss and the Europeans had struggled to keep their airplane up long enough to fly a circle, the Wrights were making figure eights in flights lasting up to two hours.

The Wright brothers were recognized by the world as conquerors and heroes. The Wright Model A Flyer was the their ticket to fame and fortune.

In addition to their factory in France, the Wrights sold rights to build this airplane to companies in Germany and Britain. Through 1909 the Wright Model A was known as the most dependable and safest airplane in the world. It established altitude and distance records in the U.S. and Europe.

The TA Wright Model A Flyer is ready for flight—grasp one of the toothpick landing skids and thrust it forward.

On September 17, 1908, in an accident caused by a broken propeller, Lieutenant Selfridge (see AEA p. 54) was killed. Orville Wright was giving a demonstration ride to this member of the AEA, when the propeller split, cutting control wires and causing the Model A to crash into the ground. Orville was badly injured and was unable to fly for months.

Wilbur did not return to America immediately, but stayed in Europe till Orville joined him in January 1909.

During that time Wilbur set the official record for the longest flight of 1908, and was awarded the Michelin prize of 20,000 francs. His flight was of 2 hours and 20 minutes duration, and over 150 kilometers. He also set the altitude record by flying over 350 feet from the ground. He demonstrated the Model A for King Edward of England, and King Alfonso of Spain. A new Model A was shipped directly to Italy, and was demonstrated to King Victor

Wright Model A flyer construction detail.

Emmanuel.

But the Wright contract with the U.S. Signal Corps had not been fulfilled, only extended after Orville's flying accident with Lt. Selfridge.

The Wrights knew their Model A Flyer was not fast enough to reach the 40 miles per hour requirement of the Army contract. The Wrights constructed a new, faster flyer when they returned to their Dayton workshop.

TA 1908 Model A Flyer

G   C₁,₂ L₁,₂ I   A   H   B   K₁,₂ E₁₋₄ F₁₋₄ J₁,₂ D

Alphabetical Parts Listing:

A and B are the main wings.
C 1,2 are the elevators.
D is the tail assembly.
E 1-4 are the main wing struts.
F 1-4 are the elevator struts.

G is the landing skid frame.
H 1 is the tail assembly top strap.
I is the motor.
J 1,2 are propeller mounts.
K 1,2 are propellers.
L 1,2 are seats.

Assembly of the TA 1908 Model A Flyer is identical to the assembly required for the 1905 Wright Flyer III. The major differences for both the real Wright aircraft and the TA version are:

1. Two seats were added because of the passenger requirement of the army contract.
2. A larger engine to offset the increased drag and weight.
3. The elevators decreased slightly in size.
4. The tail rudders decreased slightly in size, and were moved farther aft.

TA 1908 Model A Flyer with seats and larger engine assembled using instructions from Model III w/wide skid track.

40

Special Assembly for TA 1908 Model A.

As in the previous flyers, if camber is to be used, the bend must be made before assembly.

Assemble the entire aircraft using the instructions for the Wright Flyer III, referring back to the TA Kitty Hawk Flyer if necessary.

Use the landing skid instructions below in Step 1 on page 35 (Flyer III).

Install the seats (directions below) when you mount the engine, as done during step 3 on page 36.

The landing skid frame (**G**) should be folded with the "feet" facing in, as shown in the photo to the right.   Folding the landing skid frame "feet" out will result in a wider skid track.

Install the seats (**L1,2**) on the forward edge of the wing, one with the left edge touching the center line, the other an eighth of an inch to the right (looking head on).

Place the engine one-fourth of an inch to the left of the center-line.

Cut the toothpick tail assembly support to a one and one-fourth inch length.
Return to page 35 and 36 for all assembly instructions.

Folding the landing gear assembly outward, creating the "wide track" version, may support the wings better. Storing airplanes upside down also reduces sag.

Tuning and flying the TA Model A is identical to the previous flyers. The TA Model A requires no extra weight, but adding a little can increase glide.

Bend the landing skid frame so that the "feet" face in. The toothpick tail assembly support is one eighth of an inch longer than Flyer III. Use the instructions for Flyer III starting on page 35.

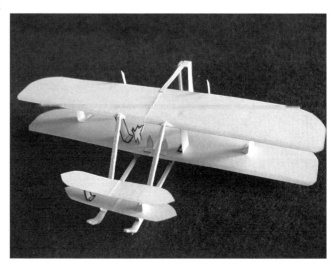

41

1909 Wright Military Flyer

The 1909 Military Flyer was smaller than the Model A. The Wrights expected the reduced size to allow the new flyer to exceed the Army requirement of carrying 2 men at 40 miles per hour. The double elevators at the front were slightly larger at 80 square feet than those on the Model A (70 sq ft). The Military Flyer was 28.9 feet long, and weighed 735 lb. See the comparison with the Wright Model A Flyer at the right.

During the trials at Ft. Myer, this airplane carried a passenger at 42.6 miles per hour over a 10 mile race course.

Military Flyer at trials, Ft Myer July 1909.

1908 Model A	**1909 Military Flyer**
Wing span: 41 ft.	Wing span: 36.5 ft.
Length: 31 ft.	Length: 28.9 ft.
Engine: 30 hp.	Engine: 30 hp.
Weight: 800 lb.	Weight: 735 lb.
Speed: 37 mph	Speed: 42.6 mph
(speed w/passenger.)	(speed w/passenger.)

The Military Flyer met all the Army requirements. A passenger was carried on a flight of over one hour and twelve minutes; this was a world record at the time. Landings and takeoffs were reliably safe, and the 1909 Military Flyer became the first airplane of the Army Signal Corps on August 2, 1909.

The Wright brothers were required to train Army pilots as part of their contract. While Lieutenant Frank Lahm and Lieutenant Benjamin Foulois had been selected for training, when Foulois was sent to Reims, France, Lt. Frederick Humphreys was picked as his replacement.

During this training, Wilbur Wright removed one of the two front elevators on the Military Flyer, and placed it behind the twin tail rudders. This tail plane was at first stationary, but then made movable, giving the Military Flyer an elevator at both the front and the back. Orville Wright was experimenting with the same concept in Germany at roughly the same time. Orville put a third elevator in place behind the rudders of a Model A Flyer. Both brothers found the elevator in the back added "pitch" stability. Adding the rear elevator made the airplane easier to control, less sensitive to movement of the front elevators.

The last change made to the Military Flyer was made by Lt. Foulois, who had learned to fly by correspondence with the Wrights. Foulois added wheels.

Wright 1909 Military Flyer

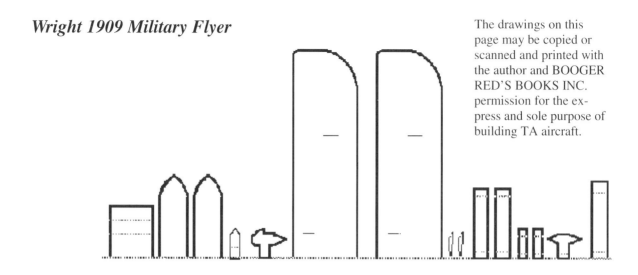

Modified Military Flyer

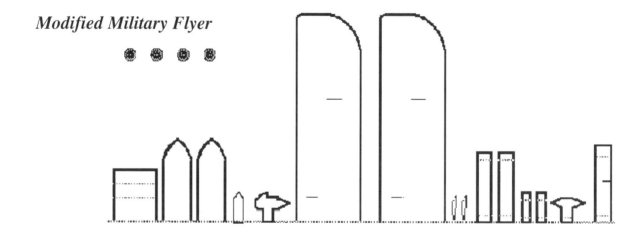

The TA 1909 Military Flyer

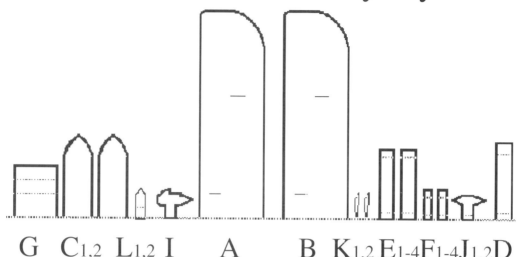

G C1,2 L1,2 I A B K1,2 E1-4 F1-4 J1,2 D

Alphabetical Parts Listing:

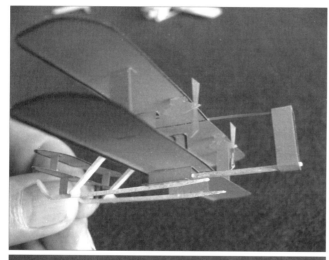

A and B are the main wings.
C 1,2 are the elevators.
D is the tail assembly.
E 1-4 are the main wing struts.
F 1-4 are the elevator struts.

*Build the TA Military Flyer using the instructions for Flyer III on pages 35 and 36. Bend the landing skid frame "feet" **out**. Use a 1 and 1/4 inch tail assembly support.*

G is the landing skid frame.
H 1 is the tail assembly top strap.
I is the motor.
J 1,2 are propeller mounts.
K 1,2 are propellers.
L 1,2 are seats.

The TA Modified Military Flyer reflects wheels and elevator changes. Wheels should be positioned as Model R (p. 83). Attach rear elevator to slot in tail using sawing motion (see A-B on p. 81.)

Curtiss and Voisin—Competition

Gliders such as those the Wright Brothers built in 1902 were to some extent copied from the successes that earlier pioneers had met. True, the Wrights set up a wind tunnel, and used their considerable scientific and engineering genius to finally solve the puzzle of flight. But their work at first was a continuation of their predecessors. In turn, the gliders that Chanute and Lilienthal flew were at least partial imitations of the successful glider designs of their predecessors.

The fact is that there was a community of interest in flying and the possibilities of flight that stretched worldwide. A good portion of the scientific community of the time was dedicated to this goal, and many of the real pioneers actually shared their information in the hope of achieving the common goal. Chanute was a valuable resource to the Wright brothers, and they purposely kept him updated throughout the early years, as he did them.

In April of 1903, Octave Chanute lectured to the Aero Club of France, introducing them to the Wrights' wing warping system, and the control surfaces that were so important to the brothers' 1902 glider. Now, the French were determined to fly first. A Captain Ferdinand Ferber (an artillery commander in France) had corresponded with Octave Chanute since 1901, and later with the Wrights. Ferber openly pled with Ernest Archdeacon, one of the founders of the Aero Club, "the airplane must not be allowed to reach successful development in America." The news in December, that the Wrights had flown at Kitty Hawk, was thus a shock and a wake up call for the French Aero Club, who then offered a cash prize to the first to fly 60 meters.

While at first the Wrights were openly exuberant over their triumph, the failure of the U.S. Government and the news media to recognize or even acknowledge the fact that controlled flight was now a reality caused the Wrights great disappointment. The Wrights made a conscious decision not to fly, but instead attempted from late 1905 through May of 1908 to sell their designs.

This disappointment turned into resentment when aircraft designers in both America and Europe began to make progress towards controlled flight using elements of what the Wrights felt were their own designs. Later, they actually sued Glen Curtiss and others for patent infringement relating to the use of ailerons and their own wing warping system.

In 1906, the French journal L'Aerophile published the Wright patent in detail. Now the French and the world had access to the Wrights' secrets.

During the period after the Wright brothers' 1903 success, and prior to their 1908 demonstrations in the United States and Europe, designers were definitely influenced by the Wright success. Although most were skeptical, to seek any and all information available about the Wright flight or aircraft to compare, test and evaluate was an essential part of the scientific method. The evidence for this sharing of knowledge is well documented, and apparent in the similarities of the successful aircraft designs of the period.

The question is do these similarities mean that many of the aircraft of the world (at that time) were just copies, or imitations? While lawsuits and litigations dragged on until World War 1, seeking to resolve many issues of this very subject, aircraft continued to evolve. It seems that the long term answer to this complex question is that new technology spawns new applications of that technology, which in turn demand new solutions and lead to further gains in technology, independently. In other words, new solutions were worked out to apply the new technology to each airplane's specific design.

While many pioneer's openly copied others designs, and borrowed their engineering solutions, their applications were many times completely original.

So, did Curtiss, Bleriot, or the Voisin brothers etc., copy or imitate the Wrights? Yes, of course they did! Just as the Wright brothers imitated their predecessors and contemporaries! There were many contributors to the rapidly growing knowledge presented by the worldwide community of pioneers of flight. But remember, that collectively, their great pioneering work, risk taking and research led to the _conquest_ of the air!

Are the words, copies and imitations, too strong or critical? There are still strong words and critical language used by admirers of Curtiss to describe the Wright patent claims. Blame is still attached by many for the myriad lawsuits that seemingly paralyzed American aviation before WW I. Bitterness caused by the wing warping and aileron patent suits kept the Wright Kitty Hawk Flyer from being displayed at the Smithsonian until 1948. Curtiss even modified and rebuilt the Langley Aerodrome, then attempted to fly it in an attempt to discredit the Wright claims of being the first to fly.

Built an ocean apart, the June Bug and the Voisin still have their similarities; biplane wings, box twin tails, front (canard) elevator.

Recognition for the Wrights' achievement was even minimized by the award of pilot's license number 1 to Glenn Curtiss in 1911. When Orville Wright was given number 4, and Wilbur was given license number 5, this was another insult to the first flyers.

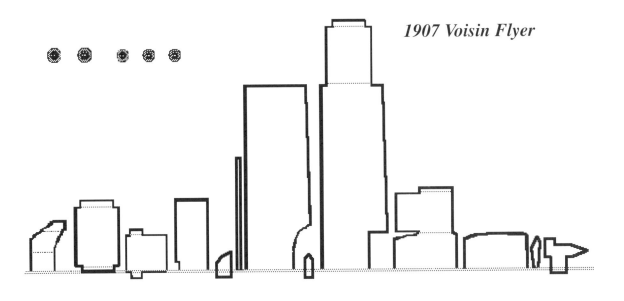

1907 Voisin Flyer

AEA June Bug

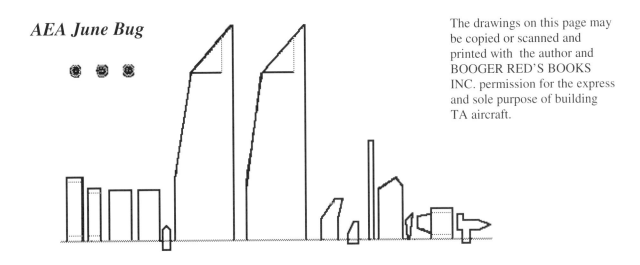

The drawings on this page may be copied or scanned and printed with the author and BOOGER RED'S BOOKS INC. permission for the express and sole purpose of building TA aircraft.

The Competitors' Solutions

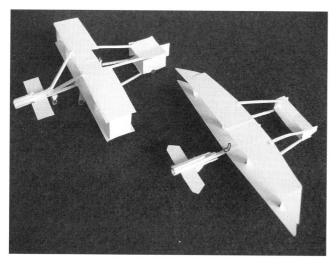

Lieutenant Selfridge of the AEA designed the June Bug after requesting and receiving patent and other information directly from the Wright brothers.

Gabriel Voisin and the Aerial Experiment Association (AEA) came up with similar solutions to the problems of stabilizing their airplanes over all three axes of flight. Front elevators gave both airplanes control over pitch. Thus, the pilot would work a lever and the elevator would force the nose of the aircraft up or down, as directed.

The biplane design provided the necessary lift with similar wing surface area (420 sq. ft. for June Bug, 434 for the Voisin) in both airplanes.

One major difference from the Voisin was the use of ailerons on June Bug's wingtips, even if the workings were primitive. The Voisin relied on box kite-type side curtains and manipulating the rudder for controlling roll. Turns in both of these aircraft were difficult according to all sources, because of these problems.

The tail assemblies for the Voisin and June Bug were of the box kite type, with the rudder or rudders trailing. Yaw, or turns to the left or right were initiated with the rudder. However when one wing dropped, the only way to correct was again with the rudder.

The Voisin had box-kite type wings and tail. For flying straight and level, it was relatively stable.

Although there were many other pioneers around the world making machines to attempt flight, the AEA and The Brothers Voisin built airplanes that actually flew and demonstrated controlled flight. In short, by 1908, there were a few airplanes that could demonstrate the straight line or limited turn flights the Wrights had demonstrated in 1903.

But this ended abruptly after the 1908 Wright demonstrations in America and France. Now, all the Wright secrets were known. By 1909, new airplanes had been designed and new challenges waited.

The Brothers Voisin

Gabriel Voisin began his flying career piloting a glider for Ernest Archdeacon of the Aero Club in 1904. His glide was successful and Voisin began building his own gliders. These gliders were launched by being towed behind cars at first, then behind speed boats because it was deemed safer. One of his most successful glides was witnessed and photographed near Paris. Among the spectators were Louis Bleriot and Alberto Santos-Dumont, both destined to be early heroes of the air.

Voisin formed a partnership with Louis Bleriot, and the pair produced some radical designs that were not successful. The two split when their compromised designs showed no promise of flight whatsoever.

Voisin was joined by his brother Charles to establish an aircraft factory, The Brothers Voisin. The two produced custom-built airplanes for designers and dreamers, although business was slow till they sold their first box-kite type design. Their customer was Leon Delagrange, a wealthy Parisian sculptor. While he had designed his own idea of a flying machine for Voisin to build, the brothers were able to persuade him to try their design.

Trying out the new machine, Charles Voisin made a controlled flight of about 260 feet, on March 30, 1907.

Delagrange learned to fly his airplane and soon was attempting turns. In 1908, Delagrange took a female passenger, Therese Peltier, for a ride in his Voisin. Peltier was the first woman ever to go up in an airplane. Delagrange became one of the most successful early European flyers.

Orders for Voisin airplanes increased dramatically. Henry Farman, a well known English bicycle and automobile racer, gave the brothers an order for a 50 horsepower airplane that could fly one kilometer. The brothers were able to fill the order, and delivered the new airplane on October 7, 1907. Henry Farman made the first successful flight himself, with only whatever verbal instruction the Voisins could offer.

On January 13, 1908, Henry Farman made the first circular flight in European history with his Voisin biplane. He flew more than one kilometer, which earned him a 50,000 franc prize that had been offered by the Aero Club, although the flight lasted only one minute and twenty eight seconds.

Gabriel Voisin stated triumphantly, "At this moment none of our competitors was worrying us. We were indeed the only people in the world able to offer, to those wanting to fly, an airplane capable of flying more or less correctly, and although an army of plagiarists tried their best to equal us, not one could claim to approach the results we obtained."

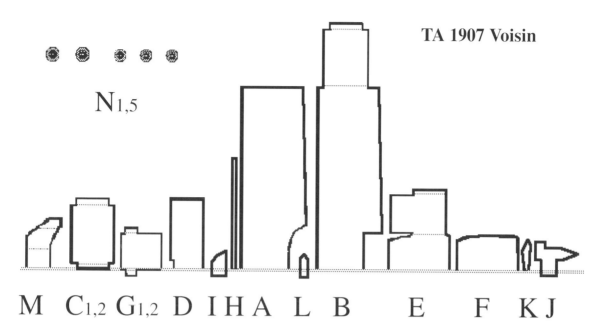

$N_{1,5}$

M $C_{1,2}$ $G_{1,2}$ D I H A L B   E   F K J

A is the bottom wing.
B is the top wing assembly.
C1,2 are wing struts.
D is the elevator.
E is the upper tail assembly.
F is the lower tail plane.
G is the rudder.

H1,2 are tail assembly top straps.
I is the front wheel assembly.
J is the engine assembly.
K is the propeller.
L is the seat.
M is the landing gear assembly.
N1-5 are wheels.

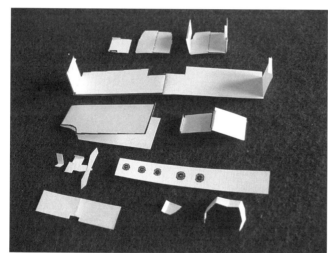

Shown top to bottom: Tail assembly, 3 parts, folded. Top wing assembly with folded struts. Lower wing, and folded struts. Seat, engine assembly, wheels. Elevator, wheel assembly, landing gear.

Step 1. Copy, scan and print, or trace the TA 1907 Voisin Flyer on page 47.
Step 2. Crease, then firmly bend the paper at the fold line.
Step 3. Cut out the parts starting at the fold line, except the wheels (**N1-5**).
Step 4. Make the bends for each part on the dotted lines, starting at the dotted line furthest from the original fold line. Cut the struts apart <u>after</u> the folds are made.
Step 5. Cut the wheels out first in a strip as shown in the photo at left. Use the blank end of the strip to turn the wheel strip as you cut.

TA 1907 Voisin Flyer

Add camber to the TA Voisin Flyer before folding the wingtip struts that are part of the upper wing assembly. Make sure the camber bend is in front of and does not include the strut on the upper wing.

Again, this flyer assembly requires you to know the concepts needed to build the TA Bleriot and first Wright flyers. If you skipped—you may need to go back. Congratulations, you are almost a journeyman TA aircraft engineer.

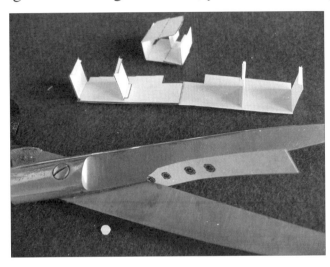

*Identify the rear of the tail assembly now. The upper tail assembly (**E**) has struts attached. The "feet" of those struts are at the front of the tail assembly. Remember both the tail and the wing assemblies are upside down at this stage of construction! Wing struts are in position.*

Step 1. Place the upper tail assembly (**E**) upside down on the work surface, so that the printed side is up. The "feet" on the side struts of the upper tail assembly are at the front. Glue the rudder (**G**) in place on the original fold line at the rear of the upper tail assembly (**E**). The rear of the rudder's "foot" should be flush with the trailing edge of **E**, and the rudder protrude to the rear of the tail.

Glue the top side of the lower tail plane (**F**) to the printed side of the upper tail plane strut. Leave the other side unglued for now. The bottom side of **F** is printed, and should face up when in place.

Place the top wing assembly (**B**) on your work surface with the printed side up. Glue the wing struts (**C1,2**) in position three-fourths of an inch from the original fold line at the center of the wing. The leading edge of the struts should be just be just behind the cambered leading edge of the wing, paralleling the attached outside wing struts. Allow the wing struts to dry.

Step 2. Carefully place glue on the "foot" of the remaining tail assembly strut, and press the lower tail plane (**F**) in place, with the edge of the tail plane forming a right angle with the tail assembly strut. When dry, glue the remaining rudder foot to the centerline of the tail plane.

Line up the engine assembly (**J**), and glue it in place at the rear (trailing edge) of the lower wing (**A**). Glue the seat (**L**) in place on the wing edge, in

51

front of the engine.

Straighten up the wing struts, placing each one at a right angle to the upper wing assembly (**B**). Carefully align the lower wing (**A**), and gently press it into position over the top wing assembly. Make the outside struts flush with the wing tips of the upper wings. Allow these assemblies to dry.

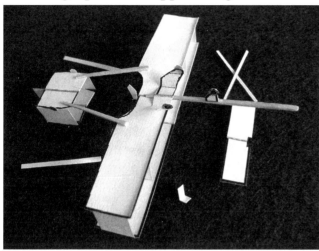

Press the "camber" fold of the bottom wing flat with the fuselage toothpick, when gluing it into position. Using the tail assembly in its approximate position, and the wing centerlines, align the tail assembly supports while gluing.

Step 3. Clip the small, rear end off a toothpick so that two inches remain. The wider end will form the front of the fuselage, with the beveled edge away from the wing.

With the wing assembly (**A**) upside down on the work surface, glue the top, narrow end of the fuselage to the bottom wing on the center, original fold line at a 90 degree or right angle. Press the fuselage in position, with the rear tip one-eighth of an inch from the trailing edge of the wing. Flatten the camber fold, gluing the wing flat to the toothpick fuselage.

Clip two one and three-eighth inch pieces from the narrow

end of toothpicks for use as tail assembly supports. Use the beveled side as the bottom. Place glue on the wider, top end and glue to the bottom rear wing assembly. The toothpick tail assembly support should overlap the wing one-eighth of an inch. For alignment purposes only, orient the tail assembly behind the wing in its approximate position. Angle the tail assembly supports so that the rear end of the supports is over the front, outer edge of the tail assembly.

When the tail assembly supports dry, glue the tail assembly (**E**) to the rear, flat top of the toothpick tail assembly supports, using an eighth of an inch overlap. Allow to dry.

Glue two of the smaller wheels (**M3-5**) to the tail assembly, one on each side where the tail strut "feet" connect with the lower tail plane (**F**). The wheels should protrude one-sixteenth of an inch below the tail plane.

Reverse the folds on one side of the landing gear assembly (**M**), and glue the large wheels (**N1,2**) to the landing gear assembly. Glue the assembly to the bottom wing, centering the original fold line on the toothpick fuselage, at the leading edge of the lower wing.

Glue the remaining wheel to the front wheel assembly (**I**) and allow it to dry. Glue the front wheel assembly five-eighths of an inch in front of the wing, to the lower surface of the fuselage. It should not to touch the landing surface.

Bottom view of 1907 Voisin with rear wheels and wheel assemblies attached.

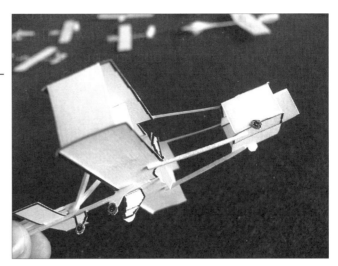

Glue the elevator (**D**) in place three-fourths of an inch from the leading edge of the lower wing. The notched edge of the elevator should be forward.

The tail assembly is heavy, and far enough to the rear to necessitate using a lot of toothpick weight to move the center of gravity forward for gliding.

Step 4. Glue the tail assembly top straps (**N1,2**) into position, directly above the tail assembly supports.

Select two straight toothpicks for use as airframes. These serve two functions in the TA Voisin Flyer. They provide rigidity and strength to the center of the upper wing, and weight.

Glue the wide, heavier end of the toothpick to the fuselage just behind the elevator. Place a dollop of glue on the forward edge of the upper wing, in line with the tail assembly top straps. Rest the top of the toothpick airframe against the top wing in that dollop of glue. Repeat this with the airframe on the other side.

Glue toothpick weights in place in front of the airframe. These weights can be up to seven-eighths inch long. Start with four weights of this length and add more as needed. Use the standard tuning instructions.

The TA 1907 Voisin Flyer is a little heavier than many TA flyers. To counter this you may have to increase lift by bending the trailing edge of the wings downward slightly. Be careful to increase the lift the same on both sides. Give the front edge of the elevator a small upward twist. The TA 1907 Voisin is an effective flyer, as the box-kite type side curtains add flight stability.

The Aerial Experiment Association

On October 1, 1907, Alexander Graham Bell, the inventor of the telephone, formed a group called the Aerial Experiment Association or AEA. The group consisted of F. W. Baldwin, J. A. D. McCurdy, Glenn Curtiss, and U.S. Army Lieutenant Thomas E. Selfridge.

All were devoted to the goal they had set: building a successful flying machine capable of carrying a man.

Glenn Curtiss was a noted motor cycle racer, who had driven a motor cycle at a speed of 136.2 miles per hour. He built his own engine for that and most of his motorcycles, and was thus called on to build engines for flying machines for early lighter-than-air craft.

He had already worked with F. W. Baldwin on the California Arrow, a dirigible powered by a 5 horsepower Curtiss engine. Curtiss also built an engine for a large army dirigible, where he also worked with Baldwin.

Bell himself had also purchased an engine from Curtiss, for an experimental "kite" aircraft in an earlier attempt at powered flight. Glenn Curtiss was the group's "Director of Experiments," and would provide and maintain the engines for the group's experiments.

The group experimented with kites at first, including one that could carry a man. But the Wrights had flown years before, and the group elected Lieutenant Selfridge as project director for the groups first airplane. Selfridge wrote to the Wright brothers for information on basic aerodynamics and wing construction. The Wright brothers answered his questions and referred Selfridge to technical papers they had published, and to the specifications of one of their patents.

The first airplane the AEA built was called "Redwing," because it was covered with red silk. It was powered by a 40 horsepower Curtiss engine.

Redwing did not have wing warping, or ailerons, and thus had no "roll" control. With F. W. Baldwin at the controls, it flew 319 feet on its first flight. On the second flight Redwing crashed and was damaged beyond repair.

The AEA built a second aircraft, and this time moveable control surfaces at the wingtips acted as ailerons. This airplane was called Whitewing, and used the same 40 horsepower engine from Redwing.

Baldwin flew Whitewing first on May 18, 1908. Lieutenant Selfridge also made two flights, but when Curtiss made his first flight Whitewing showed its real potential. Curtiss was able to work the primitive ailerons to make turns during a flight of 1,017 feet. McCurdy crashed Whitewing when his turn came. Each of these men had to teach himself to fly, with only the best explanations possible from those who went before him.

Curtiss was appointed project director for the next airplane. The design was very similar to Whitewing, and used the same engine. Alexander Graham Bell named the airplane because he thought it darted about like a "June Bug."

With Curtiss as pilot, the June Bug flew 3420 feet at 38.9 miles per hour. This was a resounding success for the AEA, although compared to the Wrights controlled flights, it was primitive.

The June Bug was the only airplane entered in the trophy race for the first airplane to make a public flight of one kilometer (3,281 feet). Scientific American magazine had originally offered the trophy thinking the Wright brothers would quickly claim it. But the Wright brothers were finally getting their break with the offer of an army contract, and were too busy rebuilding Flyer III with seats and a larger engine. The Wrights airplanes were still launched on a rail with the catapult designed in 1904. Although the Wrights could have converted to wheels, they felt their priority had to be meeting the contract demands of the U.S. Army and the French.

AEA June Bug won the Scientific American Trophy for the first public flight in U.S..

The one kilometer demonstration course was a straight flight in which a piloted airplane needed to take off, fly the necessary distance, and land safely. The June Bug was more than capable, and according to Curtiss, "I might have gone a good deal farther as the motor was working beautifully and I had the machine under perfect control, but to have prolonged the flight would have meant a turn in the air or passing over a number of large trees." On July 4, 1908, Glenn Curtiss and the AEA won the Scientific American Trophy for the first public flight in the United States.

In early 1909, Curtiss and his new partner A. M. Herring formed their own aircraft company, and he left the Aerial Experiment Association. It was a very abrupt departure, and the AEA was left without a mechanic that understood the Curtiss engine. Because of Curtiss's departure and the loss of Lt. Selfridge in the 1908 Wright crash, the AEA was disbanded.

The new company drew immediate attention, and investors, thanks to Herring. Herring promised patent rights and engineering expertise for his part in the Herring-Curtiss Company. An airplane was ordered by Aeronautic Society of New York, which Curtiss was able to deliver by June, 1909. The new airplane was the Golden Flyer, and cost $5,000. It was the first airplane sold in America. Curtiss won his second Scientific American Trophy with this plane.

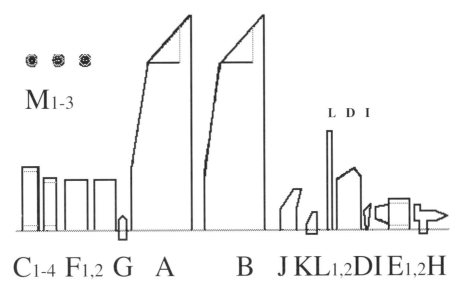

M1-3

C1-4 F1,2 G A   B JKL1,2DI E1,2H

A is the top wing.
B is the bottom wing.
C1,2 are inside wing struts.
C3,4 are outside wing struts.
D is the front elevator.
E1,2 are rudder and tail plane struts.
F are the tail planes.

G is the seat.
H is the engine assembly.
I is the propeller.
J is the main landing gear.
K is the front landing gear.
M1-3 are wheels.
L1,2 are the tail assembly top straps.

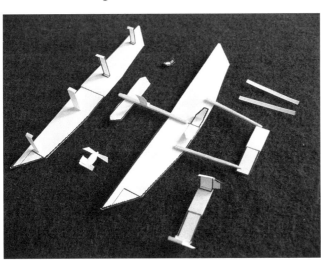

Glue the long struts one-half inch from the centerline, the short struts just inside the aileron cuts of the wings. The front edge of both sets should begin at the front of the aileron cuts. Use the tail plane for positioning the tail supports.

Assembling the TA AEA June Bug is very much like the TA Voisin. Refer to the TA Voisin.

No camber should be added to this airplane because of the curved nature of the dihedral of the lower and anhedral (wing-tips are lower than root) of the upper wing.

Cut out and prepare the parts as shown in the photo at the left.

The fuselage toothpick (large end forward) should be one and five-eighth inches long. The toothpick (small end of the tooth-pick) tail supports should bc onc and one-fourth inch long.

The fuselage should overlap the wing by three-eighths inch.

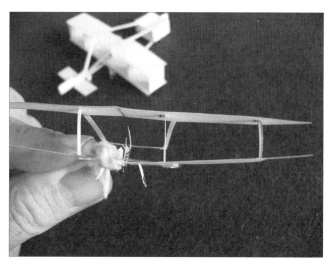

The lower wing has dihedral, meaning the wing tips are <u>higher</u> than the roots. The upper wing has anhedral, meaning the wing tips are <u>lower</u> than the roots.

With the lower wing (**B**) print side up on your work surface, glue the tail support toothpicks to the wing at the outer edge (from the centerline) of the wing's longest chord. The wide end of the tail support should overlap the wing an eighth of an inch; use the tail plane (**F**) to adjust the angle as shown in the picture on the previous page.

Glue the elevator (**D**) to the front of the toothpick fuselage, one-eighth inch from the tip. Allow these to dry.

Glue the seat (**G**), and the engine assembly (**H**) to the top surface of the lower wing (**B**).

Add dihedral to the lower wing by first carefully bending the wings upward starting at the center. Make sure the upward bend at the front of the wing root is the same as the bend at the rear of the wing root to ensure equal lift. Apply anhedral to the top wing (**A**) in the same careful manner.

With the upper wing print side up, straighten the struts carefully, then align the wings and glue the lower wing (**B**) into position.

The ailerons on the TA June Bug can be adjusted to provide balanced lift for straight flight, or lift and drag for turns.

Glue the wing end of the tail support straps (**L**) in position first, and allow them to dry. Align them directly above the toothpick tail supports. When dry, glue the tail end of the tail support straps in position.

Glue the wheels (**M**) on the main landing gear (**J**), and then the front landing gear (**K**).

Add approximately five three-fourth inch toothpick blocks for weight to the front toothpick fuselage. Tuned, the TA June Bug flies very well indeed.

57

The First International Air Meet

The first international air meet was organized by the city of Reims and the French Champagne industry. The meet was seen as good advertising, a glorious introduction to the supremacy of French aviation, and a grand social event with lots of champagne. The event's official title was "The Grande Semaine d'Aviation de la Champagne" or "The Champagne Region's Great Aviation Week."

Prizes of 200,000 francs ($40,000) were offered by the premier champagne makers for speed, distance, altitude and passenger carrying. The largest prize was the Grand Prix, for distance, with a purse of 50,000 francs.

Perhaps the most prestigious award was the International Aviation Cup, offered by James Gordon Bennett. Bennett was the publisher of both The New York Herald and The Paris Herald, and provided a silver trophy (with a Wright Flyer perched atop), and a cash prize of 25,000 francs for the fastest time over a 20 kilometer course.

The event lasted a week, beginning on Sunday, August 22, 1909. Attendance was estimated at over half a million spectators. Nobility, foreign diplomats, ambassadors, generals and admirals from all over Europe and America were among the throngs. The event became annual after its huge first success, until it became impractical with the advent of World War I.

Some of the fliers at Reims had little or no actual flight time. In fact at least one had never flown at all. One Frenchman, Ruchonnet, who would fly one of the Antoinettes, had never even sat in an airplane. On Friday before the meet he taxied for twenty minutes. On Saturday he bent his landing gear making a few short flights. By Tuesday, during the meet, he circled the field on a mile-long flight. Another flier had just received his airplane from his father as a high school graduation present.

Eugene Lefebvre, a representative of the Wright factory in France, had just taught himself to fly. His longest flight prior to Reims was only seventeen minutes, yet he qualified to represent France for the Gordon Bennett Trophy.

Of the thirty-eight airplanes entered, only twenty-three actually made it into the air. Among those entered were six Wright Model As built in France, four Bleriot XIs, nine Voisin aircraft, four Farman airplanes, four Antoinette VIIs, a (Robert Esnault-Pelterie) REP monoplane airplane, several Demoiselle 20s, and at least one Breguet I tractor biplane. The lone American entry was Glenn Curtiss's Reims Racer.

Early 1909 had seen several new airplanes and at least a couple of dozen fliers meet the challenge of controlled flight. Most were coming to Reims.

Antoinette VII

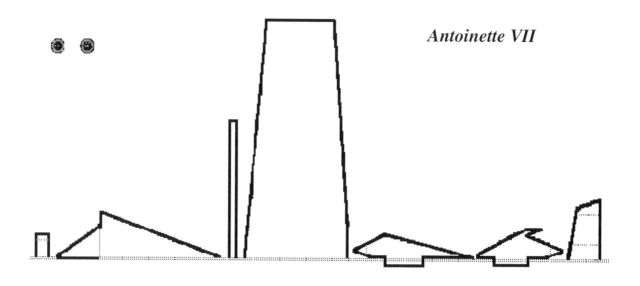

Bleriot XII

1909 Antoinette VII

Leon Levavasseur designed the Antoinette in 1908. Levavasseur was both an artist and an engineer. His airplane was named for the teenage daughter of his business partner. Antionette's engine was also designed by Levavasseur, a water-cooled, fifty horsepower fuel-injected unit of very advanced design.

The Antoinette IV was derived from the Antoinette II, which first flew in February of 1908. Antoinette IV utilized ailerons for maintaining control for roll in turns, and maintaining level flight. The Antoinette IV was not easy to maneuver, having some difficulty with turns, and requiring constant attention to the controls. Antoinette IV was more difficult to fly in windy, gusty, or stormy weather, and pilots generally stayed on the ground if there was any threat of weather.

Antoinette VII utilized wing warping, demonstrating the adaptability and effectiveness of the Wright system. Many of the European flyers switched to wing warping after Wilbur Wright's demonstration of controlled flight in 1908.

The Antoinette VII was a large airplane, with a wingspan of 46 feet.

Hubert Latham made an unsuccessful attempt at crossing the English Channel in 1909 in an Antoinette VII. On June 19th Latham took off and flew straight off the edge of a cliff. He continued over the channel, but his engine began acting up and finally died. From his elevation of about 1000 feet he was able to glide down toward a torpedo boat destroyer.

Although the Antoinette was recovered, it was too badly damaged for further flying. Latham was supported by Leon Levavasseur in his channel crossing attempt, and a second Antoinette was sent for. It arrived and Latham prepared for a second attempt. While he slept one morning, Louis Bleriot took off at 4:30 a.m., and conquered the English Channel in his Model XI.

Hubert Latham went on to set the altitude record at Reims in 1909.

The Antoinette was also built in Germany under license by Albatros. It was popular at air shows and competitions all over Europe and America. Antoinette was a beautiful and graceful design according to observers, and some carried two or even three passengers.

The TA Antoinette VII has only seven paper parts, and is fairly simple to build. It is capable of very long glides because it is relatively light, and has a longer wing span and larger wing area than many TA gliders.

TA 1909 Antionette VII

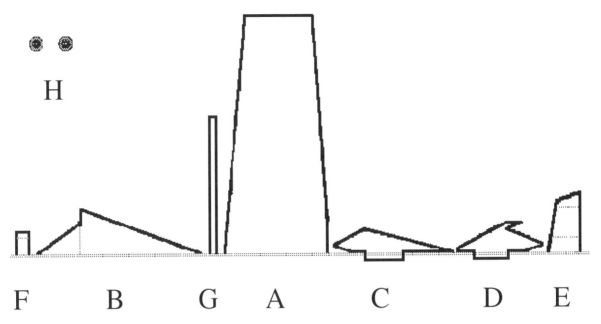

F   B   G   A   C   D   E

A is the main wing.
B is the tail plane and elevator.
C is the rudder and vertical tail.
D is the tail rudder/tail skid.

E is the main landing gear.
F is the wing brace.
G is the bracing strap.
H1,2 are wheels.

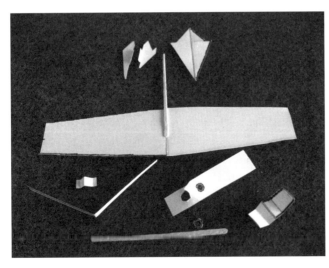

TA Antoinette VII requires skills you have learned on prior gliders. Be sure that you add camber to the wing before beginning construction. Glue the tail support toothpick to the wing with the beveled side away from the wing.

Cut out and make the necessary folds in the same way as previous TA gliders. Add camber to the wing before beginning construction.

Building the TA Antoinette VII is similar to the TA Bleriot XI. Refer to those instructions if necessary.

This glider requires two toothpicks for the fuselage. Glue the wide end of one toothpick to the wing centerline for the tail support, as shown in the photo at the left. It should overlap the trailing wing edge by five-eighths of an inch, with the beveled side of the toothpick away from the wing.

The camber fold of the wing is protected from interference with the front fuselage section by the thickness of the rear toothpick fuselage. See Bleriot photo p. 65.

Step 1. Place the tail plane and elevator (**B**) printed side up on your work surface. Glue the tail plane support toothpick in place on the tail plane with a one-half inch overlap on the tail plane centerline.

Glue the front toothpick fuselage section in place. The small end of the front fuselage should be flush with the trailing edge of the main wing (**A**), with the beveled edge away from the wing. The wide end of the toothpick should protrude from the front one and one-eighth inch. Allow it to dry.

Glue the landing gear in position on the front toothpick fuselage, even with the leading edge of the wing. Glue the wheels on the main landing gear.

Cut a one and one-eighth inch piece from the wide end of a toothpick to serve as an emergency landing skid. Bend it to a 30 degree angle and seal the bend with glue. When dry, glue it to the bottom edge of the forward fuselage.

Smear a small amount of glue on the foot of the tail rudder/skid (**D**) and position it on the centerline of the tail plane, with the rudder fold line (at the small, blunt end of **D**) even with the elevator fold line.

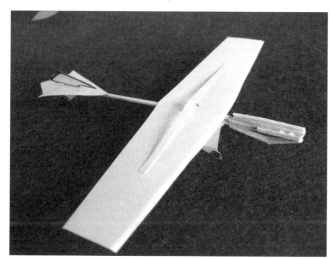

Four one and one-eighth inch toothpick weights should be enough weight.

Step 2. Turn the glider right side up, print side down. Smear glue on the foot of the rudder and vertical tail (**C**) and position it on the centerline of the tail plane. The rudder fold line should be even with the elevator fold line.

Glue the wing brace (**F**) into position at mid wing. Allow it to dry, then glue the center of the bracing strap (**G**) into position. When dry, glue each end of the bracing strap into position. The wing should have some dihedral.

The 1909 Bleriot XII

Louis Bleriot's first experimental airplanes were failures, just like all the early attempts until the Wrights. But Bleriot learned from his errors. He tried a tail first (canard) monoplane with wings shaped like a dove's. This plane was powered by a 24 horsepower engine in the rear. On its first flight it nearly killed the pilot that Bleriot had hired. The man quit and warned everyone else to stay away from Bleriot. Gabriel Voisin knew from first-hand experience that Bleriot's initial models had no chance of flying. But Louis Bleriot was determined, and just kept trying out his ideas until he got one to work. Failures were a lot more common than successes in the early years of flight.

Bleriot's sixth airplane looked somewhat similar to Langley's "aerodrome," and was called "The Dragonfly." It had movable wingtips, to function as ailerons, and a partially moveable vertical stabilizer. Bleriot also depended upon being able to shift his weight to stabilize his airplane. He made initial flights of up to 150 meters.

Bleriot felt he needed only more power to make the Dragonfly fly. He replaced the 24 hp engine with a larger, more powerful one in September of 1907, and broke his record with a flight of 184 meters.

His seventh airplane had the same wing setup. However, when unsuccessful, he began experimenting with the rear wing. Eventually it was moved to the rear of the fuselage and reduced in size. He wrecked this plane in 1907.

In 1908 Bleriot built the first true monoplane, his eighth try for a successful flyer. With this aircraft, the Bleriot design began to look like more modern monoplanes, although it still had a long way to go to be as stable and reliable as the Wright airplanes.

From experience with this airplane, Bleriot built his first Model XI, as well as the Model XII that he raced at Reims in 1909.

When Glenn Curtiss arrived in France, he heard that Bleriot had "installed an eight cylinder motor of 80 hp on one of his light monoplanes. When I (Curtiss) learned of this, I believed my chances (of winning) were very slim indeed."

Bleriot Model XII.

The Bleriot XII had a 32.8 foot wingspan, and was powered by a 60 hp engine, making it one of the most powerful airplanes in the world. Bleriot deliberately designed this airplane to carry a passenger as well as race for speed, because passenger carrying was one of the challenges of the Reims meet.

D E B G C H I J A F

A is the wing.

B is the tail plane.

C is the tail fin/rudder.

D is the elevator and skid assembly.

E is the elevator.

F is the landing gear assembly.

G is the seat assembly.

H is the aileron.

I is the wing bracc.

J is the bracing strap.

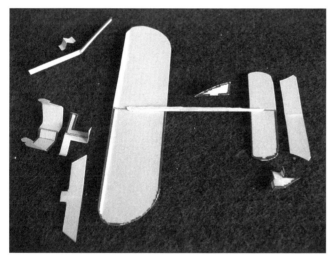

The fuselage has two parts like the Antoinette, with the front part protecting the forward camber fold of the wing.

The TA Bleriot Model XII requires several different assembly techniques from the Model XI. This model had the pilot seated below the wing, ailerons that were fastened to the rear and below the pilot, and a separate elevator to the rear and under the tail plane.

The rear toothpick fuselage section should be cut from the thin end of a toothpick one and three-fourths inch long, and should be glued to the bottom of both the wing and the tail plane. The beveled side should face away from the wing, while the wider, un-beveled end should overlap the wing by five-eighths of an inch. Overlap the tail plane (**B**) by one-eighth inch.

For the front fuselage cut the wide end of a toothpick to a length of one and one-half inches, and glue it to the bottom surface of the rear fuselage toothpick, with an overlap of one-fourth of an inch. Allow this assembly to dry.

Attach the landing gear assembly (**F**) to the bottom of the front fuselage toothpick one-eight of an inch forward of the leading wing edge. The landing gear assembly should not contact the wing at all.

The seat assembly (**G**) should be glued between the landing gear legs, just above the wheels. The seat back should be bent up, toward the wing, but should not touch the wing or fuselage.

The projection on the elevator (**H**) should be glued to the rear edge of the seat.

One inch sections may be added as landing skids to the landing gear. These should be bent

Note the front fuselage section is glued to the bottom of the rear fuselage section.

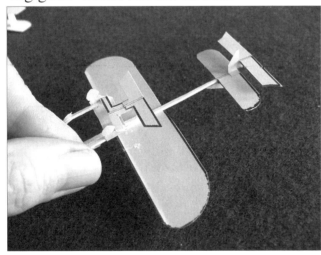

Note the elevator and tail skid assembly. The landing gear glue to fuselage only.

in the same manner as the skids for the Wright Flyers, one-fourth inch from the wide end, and sealed with glue. Glue the skids on each side of the landing gear, as far forward as possible.

The landing skids protrude farther forward than the frame of the original Model 12. Alternately, reduce them to one-half inch, and add more nose weights.

Center and glue the wing brace (**I**), then add the bracing strap (**J**) when the brace is dry.

The elevator and tail skid assembly (**D**) foot should be glued in position on the center line of the bottom surface of the tail plane as shown in the photo above. The rear edge of the mounting foot should be flush with the trailing edge of the tail plane. The elevator should be centered on the centerline of the tail skid and tail plane, and glued in position.

The TA Bleriot Model XII has more surfaces, which without careful tuning can cause a loss of gliding performance from excessive drag. If the landing skids are used, three toothpick blocks of three-fourths of an inch length should be enough weight. Try five if the skids are not used. Use the regular tuning methods on all flight surfaces.

Demoiselle 20

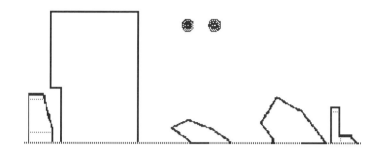

Farman III

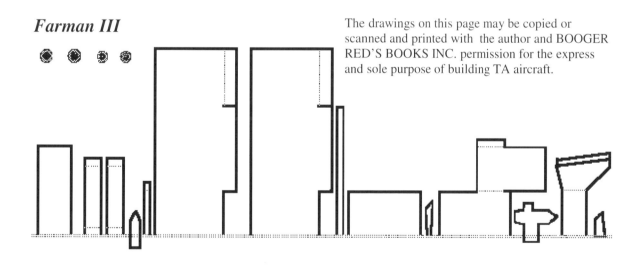

The drawings on this page may be copied or scanned and printed with the author and BOOGER RED'S BOOKS INC. permission for the express and sole purpose of building TA aircraft.

Santos-Dumont Demoiselle 20

Alberto Santos-Dumont, a Brazilian-born pioneer of the air, began his flying career in balloons and progressed to dirigibles. He graduated to gliders in 1904 after successfully impressing all of France with his dirigibles and navigation skills.

Santos-Dumont built an airplane he called 14-bis, or 14-encore, since it would be suspended from his Number 14 dirigible. The dirigible was to lift the airplane into the air, where it would be tested.

The 14-bis was a canard, so named for its resemblance to a duck. The airplane had box-kite rudder and elevator combination that projected forward like the head and neck of a waterfowl in flight. Box-kite type wings similar to the Voisin glider were to the rear, followed only by the engine and propeller in a pusher design. While 14-bis had no ailerons or wing warping, some stability was provided by severe dihedral, with the lower wing tips close to the level of the upper wing root.

While the testing of 14-bis suspended from the dirigible was unsuccessful, Santos-Dumont continued experimenting with 14-bis. In 1906 he replaced the 24 hp engine with a 50 horsepower one. On October 23, 1906, Alberto Santos-Dumont made the longest powered flight recorded in Europe. He flew 722 feet in 21.2 seconds, and was awarded the Aero Club's prize for flying 60 meters. That Aero Club prize had stood unclaimed from nearly the time of the Wrights' first flight.

14-bis was not capable of controlled flight, however, and Santos-Dumont abandoned it after a short hop in April, 1907.

Santos-Dumont's 1909 Demoiselle 20 was one of the world's first successful airplanes. It was constructed of bamboo and canvass, and powered by a 28 horsepower motor. Several of these aircraft were sold at Reims, and notable flyer Roland Garros later gave impressive aerial demonstrations in one.

After Reims, France, in 1909, 40 Demoiselle airplanes were sold.

Santos-Dumont had set out to build an airplane that the ordinary man could afford. Forty Demoiselles were sold within 6 months of the Reims, even though the airplane was tricky and dangerous to fly. Her nickname was Infuriated Grasshopper.

The Demoiselle 20 was flown in America, and many countries around the world, although it was never popular with pilots.

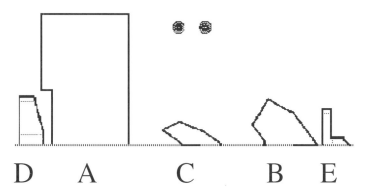

D   A   C   B   E

A is the main wing.
B is the tail plane/elevator.
C is the rudder.

D is the landing gear assembly.
E is the seat assembly.
F1,2 are wheels.

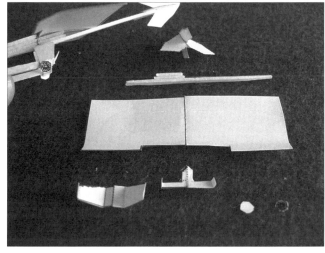

Note the toothpick blocks on the upper fuselage for mounting the wing. The upper left Demoiselle shows the wing in place on the toothpick blocks.

The TA Dumoiselle consists of only seven paper parts, the toothpick fuselage, and skids. Three-fourth inch toothpick blocks for skids, and three or four one-half inch blocks for balance and glide finish this little glider.

Constructing the "telescoping" tail assembly (**B+C**) is a skill that will be used again on advanced Wright and Taube airplanes in the next chapter. <u>The cut on the rear of the tail plane fold line will slide into the cut on the fore rudder edge.</u> Apply light smears of glue to the fold line contact areas <u>after</u> aligning the flight surfaces.

Adjusting the wings' angle of attack by using toothpick blocks is also a useful concept. Cut two three-eighths inch blocks from a toothpick inside of the bevel. Glue the blocks to the toothpick fuselage on the side away from the beveled ends, one-half inch from the wider, front end.

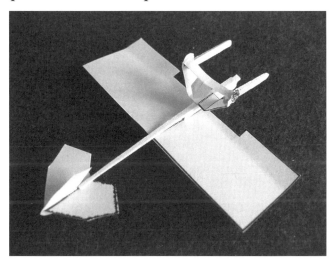

Shown upside down for assembly.

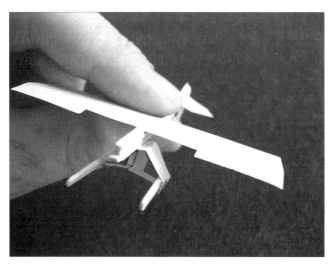

The TA Demoiselle seat and landing gear assembly is similar to the TA Bleriot XII.

The tail plane part of the tail assembly should be glued to the narrow end of the fuselage toothpick, with an eighth of an inch overlap.

Once the landing gear assembly (**D**) is in place and dry, glue one side of the seat assembly (foot) to the landing gear. The bottom of the seat assembly should be flush with the bottom of the landing gear. Glue the other side in place, then the wheels, so that they protrude downward one-sixteenth of an inch. The skids should be mounted above the seat assembly, as shown. Skids similar to the TA Bleriot XII, with a bend, can be used as an option.

The TA Demoiselle is slightly larger than the other airplanes in scale. The small paper parts are difficult to handle, even at this size. At this scale Demoiselle would have a wingspan of approximately 24 ft. The actual wingspan of the Demoiselle was 18 feet.

The real Demoiselle as well as the TA version's cruciform tail functions by making flight adjustments to the whole assembly, although the forward rudder in the TA version can be moved for fine tuning.

Farman III Biplane

Henry Farman won the distance race at Reims by flying 112 miles.

After Henry Farman's initial flying experience, he began refining and redesigning his Voisin aircraft. The Voisin design included side curtains on the wings that enhanced the airplane's box kite appearance, and provided stability. Farmen installed ailerons, and removed the side curtains from both the wings, and later the tail. A Wright type front elevator provided pitch control.

Henry Farman built Farmen III flyers for Roger Sommer and George Cockburn, which also flew at Reims.

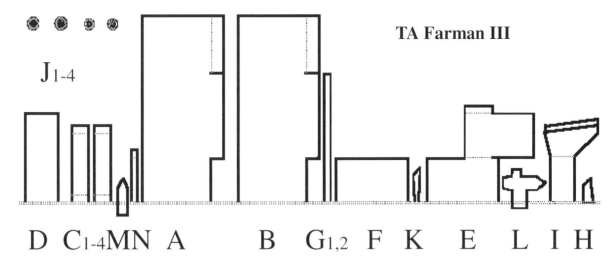

1-4

TA Farman III

D C1-4MN A   B G1,2 F K E L I H

A is the bottom wing assembly.
B is the top wing assembly.
C1-4 are the wing struts.
D is the elevator.
E is the upper tail assembly.
F is the lower tail plane.
G1,2 are the tail assembly top straps.

H1,2 are tail wheel assemblies.
I is the landing gear assembly.
J1,2 are wheels, **J3,4** are tail wheels.
K is the propeller.
L is the engine.
M is the seat.
N is the elevator tie strap.

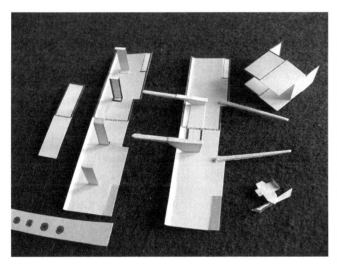

The landing skid frame is similar to early Wright airplanes. The landing skid ends can be bent up also.

The major difference between the TA Farman III and the Voisin (also June Bug) is in mounting the front elevator (**D**). Instead of a central fuselage, the TA Farmen has two lower toothpick airframes, and two upper toothpick airframes, one set on either side for mounting the elevator.

Build the wing assemblies in the same manner as the Voisin, mounting the struts on the bottom of the upper wing, and the tail assembly supports and landing gear on the lower wing bottom.

Bend the landing skid frame (**I**) feet inward. Glue the one and one-fourth inch toothpick landing skids on the side of the skid frame feet toward the wing. The tail assembly support toothpicks should be one and three-eighths inches cut from the narrow end of toothpicks. Use a one-eighth inch overlap for landing skids and tail assembly supports alike.

70

The tail assembly, engine assembly, landing gear and lower airframe are in place.

The lower toothpick airframes should be one and one-fourth inch long, cut from the wide end of toothpicks. Glue the narrower end of one to the landing skid with a one-fourth inch overlap, with the rear end in contact with the landing gear foot, touching the end of the landing skid. The angle should be approximately 30 degrees from the plane of the skid. The second lower airframe should be glued to the other side in the same manner, with the second angle matching the first as close to exactly as possible. Allow these assemblies to dry.

Glue the elevator tie strap (**N**) feet over the top, wide end of the lower toothpick airframe on each side. Make the top surface of the tie strap parallel to the wing surface and the tail surface, so that the elevator when glued to this surface will be at the same angle of approach as the wing and tail surfaces.

Glue the large wheels (**J1,2**) to the outer surface of the landing gear assembly, so that it protrudes below one-sixteenth inch.

Glue the tail wheel assemblies (**H1,2**) to the side of the tail assembly (**E**) where the strut attaches to the lower tail plane, so that the pointed end points

The elevator (D) will be glued to the level surface of the elevator tie strap.

downward, and front makes a right angle to the tail assembly. The tail wheel assemblies should extend down beyond the lower tail plane surface one-eighth inch, while the wheels (**J3,4**) should extend downward another one-sixteenth inch.

The seat should be mounted on the centerline of the bottom wing, at the front, while the engine goes on the centerline, at the rear of the same wing.

Glue the elevator in position, centered on the wing, with the rear

The TA Farman III above require 6 one inch and two one-half inch toothpick blocks for weight to glide effectively.

edge of the elevator flush with the rear edge of the elevator tie strap.

Glue the tail assembly to straps (G1,2) in place directly above the toothpick tail assembly supports.

Glue the flat, wide end of two toothpicks to the leading edge of the top wing, directly in front of the tail assembly top straps. Place a dab of glue on either side of the leading edge of the elevator, above the lower airframes, and gently position the upper air frame.

Clip the ends from the toothpick upper airframes one-fourth inch in front of the elevator. Add weight, and tune as usual.

George Cockburn represented England in the Gordon Bennett Cup race. He and his Farman III did not finish due to engine trouble. However, Farman airplanes would continue to set altitude and endurance records at air shows through 1911.

The TA Farman III is a good flyer, as stable in flight as the original, and capable of long glides when enough weight is added.

TA Curtiss Reims Racer

TA Curtiss Reims Racer gets final check.

The TA Curtiss Reims Racer is relatively heavy considering its wing area. No additional weight is recommended, and the front elevators should be tipped back, while the tail plane should be tipped upward, providing an increased angle of attack for the wings.

As shown, the Racer requires a little more thrust than most TA gliders, needs some camber, and is sensitive to aileron adjustments. It flies like the real one.

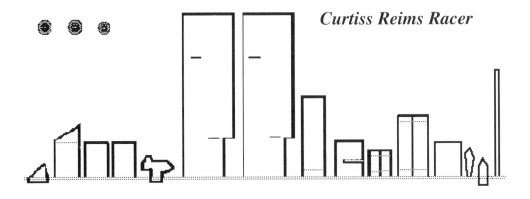

Curtiss Reims Racer

REP (Robert Esnault Peltrie)

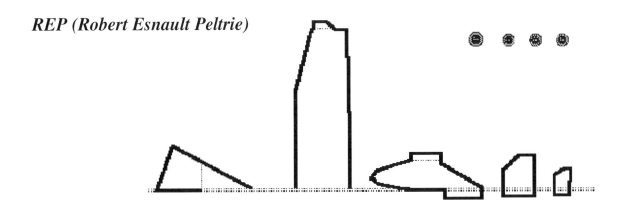

Curtiss Reims Racer

The Golden Flyer, which had been sold and delivered to the Aeronautic Society of New York, provided Curtiss with the necessary practice and flying experience he needed for his next project. Curtiss set to work to build another Golden Flyer, refined for speed and powered by a new 50 hp engine he was barely able to finish in time to ship for the Reims Air Meet. Curtiss was focused only on the Gordon Bennett speed prize, reasoning that concentrating on one goal would give him the best chance of success, and Curtiss was still the fastest motorcycle racer in the world.

The Reims Racer, and the Golden Flyer before it, were the combined result of his own flying and design experience with the AEA, and the experience of Augustus Herring, his new partner. Although it was later claimed that Herring contributed little, the basic wing setup of the Golden Flyer strongly resembled an aircraft designed and built by Herring in 1898. Gone was the curving dihedral and anhedral of the June Bug, although effective ailerons were added.

This 1898 Herring design did not fly, but had wings very similar to the Reims Racer.

The above drawing is by Douglas Rolfe, from <u>Airplanes of The World</u>.

The Reims Racer had large ailerons between the wings, at the forward edge. These provided control over roll so effectively that Curtiss' banks were noted by the French press after the Gordon Bennet Trophy race.

Pitch was provided by two elevators at the front of the Racer, while a rudder provided yaw, or directional control. A tail plane mounted with the rudder provided additional stability.

On Monday, the first day of the meet, Curtiss qualified for the race with an average speed of 43 miles per hour. Curtiss alone would represent the United States in the great race.

Five aircraft qualified for the Gordon Bennett Trophy Race. France was represented by Bleriot, Hubert Latham in his Antoinette, and Eugene LeFebure in a French built Wright Model A. England was represented by George Cockburn in a Farman III.

Curtiss' Racer won the race with an average speed of 46.5 mph. Bleriot finished only 6 seconds behind, while Latham was third and LeFebure last.

Curtiss won the Gordon Bennett Trophy and thrilled the crowd with his turns at Reims.

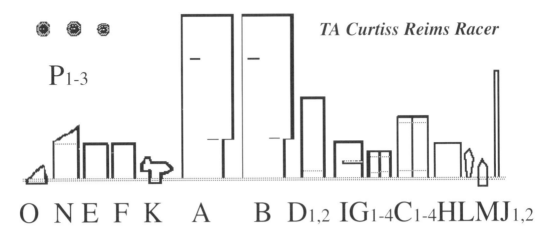

P1-3

O N E F K A B D1,2 IG1-4C1-4HLMJ1,2

A is the bottom wing assembly.
B is the top wing assembly.
C1-4 are wing struts.
D1,2 are the ailerons.
E, F are the elevators.
G1-4 are elevator struts.
H is the tail plane.
I is the tail rudder.

J1,2 are the lower tail assembly straps.
K is the engine.
L is the propeller.
M is the seat.
N is the main landing gear assembly.
O is the front landing gear assembly.
P1-3 are wheels.

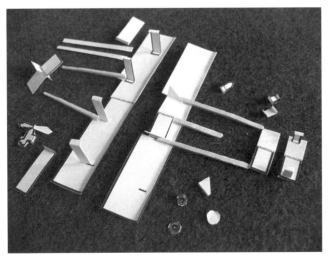

Position the wing struts using the marks printed on the lower side of the wings.

The assembly of the TA Reims Racer is similar to the TA Voisin. Refer to the basic assembly instructions on page 50.

The photo at the left shows the basic cut-out and folds complete, and the basic assembly started.

The tail assembly utilizes a "foot" folded on the inside surface of the tail rudder. The rudder should be positioned on the trailing edge of the tail plane centerline.

The tail assembly supports (narrow end of toothpicks) are one and one-fourth inch long, and should overlap the top wing (**B**) assembly and the tail assembly (**H,I**) by one-eighth inch.

The fuselage toothpick is one inch, cut from the wide end of a toothpick, and overlaps the bottom wing (**A**) by one-fourth inch. When gluing, press the toothpick flat, ignoring the camber fold of the wing.

The lower airframe toothpicks are one and one-half inch from the wide

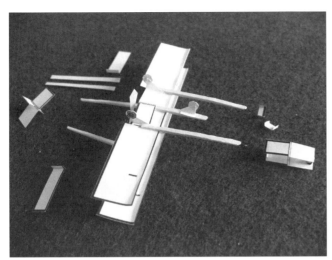

Check the spread of the tail supports with the tail plane width, and lower airframe with the elevators.

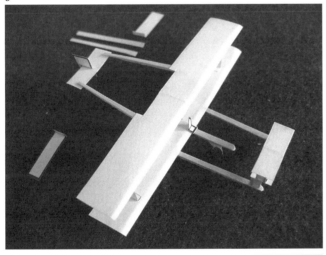

end of the toothpick. Again, press the toothpick flat against the bottom wing surface, ignoring the camber. The overlap is one-fourth inch. Check the spread of the lower airframes against the width of the elevators (**E,F**). Complete the front elevator assembly, with one set of struts as shown in the photo at the left.

Glue the main landing gear assembly (**N**) to the trailing edge of the bottom wing (**A**), centering it between the lower air frame toothpicks.

Center the seat on the leading edge of the bottom wing assembly, top surface, and place the engine behind it, on the rear edge.

Straighten the wing struts, carefully align the wings and glue the lower wing (**A**) assembly to the strut feet of the upper wing (**B**).

Glue the remaining elevator struts (**G1-4**) to the top surface of the forward end of the lower airframes. When dry, glue the elevators in place.

Glue the ailerons on the wing struts midway between the top and bottom wings.

Select straight toothpicks for upper airframes, and glue the wide ends to the cambered forward edge of the top wing. Glue the forward, thin ends to the upper, leading edge of the lower elevator. Leave one-fourth inch protruding.

Snip the upper airframe ends shorter if your glider won't pull out of dives!

TA REP (Robert Esnault Peltrie)

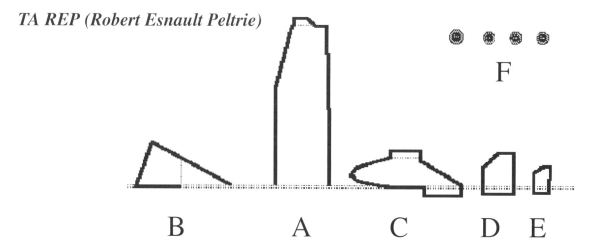

B   A   C   D   E

A is the wing.
B is the tail plane and elevator.
C is the tail assembly.

D is the front landing gear.
E is the rear landing gear.
F1 is a large wheel, F1-3 are small.

A REP monoplane flew at Reims in 1909

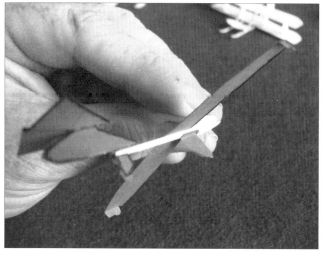

The TA REP Monoplane uses a full length toothpick for the fuselage. Glue the tail assembly's (**C**) leading "foot" to the top, non-beveled surface of the fuselage. Glue the tail plane (**B**) centerline to the rear, upper foot of the tail assembly, so that the trailing end of the foot is even with the elevator fold.

Camber the wing, then glue it in position three-fourths of an inch from the wide, front end of the fuselage. Press the fuselage firmly against the lower wing surface, flattening the camber fold!

Make the anhedral 5 degrees, bending each wing down from the wing root.

The main landing gear (**D**) should be mounted one-fourth of an inch forward of the wing, on the bottom of the fuselage. The rear landing gear mounts at the end of of the fuselage bottom. The large wheel (**F1**) mounts on the front landing gear, with a one-sixteenth inch forward and downward protrusion. The small wheels (**F2-4**) mount on the rear landing gear, and on the forward edge of the wingtip landing skids, again with no more than a one-sixteenth inch downward protrusion.

Add at least four three-fourth inch toothpick block weights for balance and glide. Tune as usual.

The REP monoplane that appeared at Reims in 1909 had a red paint job.

The first day at Reims, Sunday, August 22, was rainy and windy, with terrible flying conditions until the very end of the day. A REP monoplane

The REP had only one main landing gear, but had wheels on the wingtips as well as skids.

The above drawing is by Douglas Rolfe, from Airplanes of The World.

made an attempted takeoff in poor conditions, but became stuck in the mud. Robert Esnault-Peltrie was the designer of this little flyer. Later his aircraft introduced all-metal air frames, cantilever, internally braced wings, and radial air-cooled engines. His airplanes also featured the stick control system.

The TA version of the REP monoplane requires thorough tuning, with both wings giving equal lift in order to fly in a stable manner. The front landing gear assembly (D) is deliberately larger to provide lateral surface for some increased flight stability.

Proving They Fly

By 1910 few people in the world had seen an airplane fly, but many had heard, and it seemed that all wanted their first look. For one of the first exhibitions, in October 1909, Wilbur Wright strapped a canoe between the skids of his Model A flyer. He was to take off from Governor's Island, and fly up the Hudson River to Grant's Tomb and return. The canoe was insurance, in case of a problem over water. For this successful demonstration Wright was paid $15,000. This was half of the price the brothers received for the Military Flyer in June, for just one flight! It was plain that big money was available for what would become known as exhibition flying!

The Wright brothers had trained pilots for the Army, and their French and German airplane manufacturers. In early 1910, they began training pilots for their own exhibition team. By mid year their team was ready, and new airplanes had been designed and built. The Wright Model B was a design breakthrough for the brothers. The Wright engine, now developing 35 hp powered the B at speeds up to 45 mph. The Wrights also produced an Exhibition Flyer, with a 32 foot wing span, to compete with Curtiss and Bleriot.

The Wright Model AB was more stable in flight than the A. Versions with this modification of the "A" were flown in late '09 and early 1910, in Europe and America.

Exhibition flying was raging across Europe, with new fliers and airplanes challenging Bleriot and Farman. Soon the new flyers would come to America.

In January 1910, an international air meet was held near Los Angeles, California. Louis Paulhan flying a Farman set an altitude record of 4,165 feet. Curtiss established a world speed record of 55 mph. This was just the beginning, and pilots and airplanes were booked for flying exhibitions across the US.

The second running of the Gordon Bennet Trophy speed race would draw entries from the United States, England and France. The Wrights brought the 60 hp Baby Grand, while Curtiss entered a new 60 hp semi-monoplane. The Wrights built a Model "R" for Alexander Ogilvie of England and Englishman Claude Graham-White had installed a 100 hp engine in a Bleriot flyer. But high winds and bad weather caused many to crash, and the race was won by White's Bleriot. Curtiss dropped out, and Ogilvie's Roadster finished 3rd.

Wright Model A-B

M1,2   A   B

G   H   D1,2 L1,2 I   J1,2 C1-4 E1-4 K1,2 F

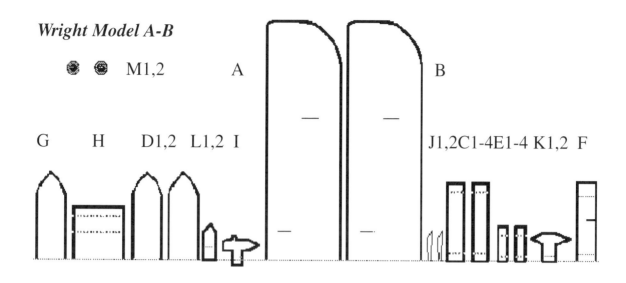

The drawings on this page may be
copied or scanned and printed
with the author and BOOGER
RED'S BOOKS INC. permission
for the express and sole purpose of
building TA aircraft.

Wright 1910 Exhibition Model   B   *Wright 1911 Vin Fiz*

O1,2   A   C1-4 H D1,2 E1-4 K1,2 M

L1,2 J   G N1,2 F   I

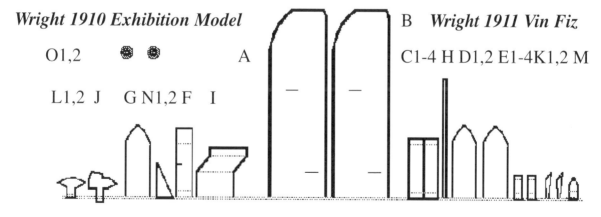

80

Wright Model A-B

Parts and special instructions:
A, B are the wings.
C1-4 are the wing struts.
D1,2 are elevators.
E1-4 are elevator struts.
F is the tail assembly.
G is the tail elevator.
H is the landing skid frame.
I is the engine.
J1,2 are propellers.
K1,2 are propeller mounts.
L1,2 are seats.
M1,2 are wheels.
Use the strip cut from between the wings for a tail assembly top strap. Tail assembly support toothpick is one and one-half inches from the narrow end of the toothpick. Landing skids are full length picks.

The A-B is assembled using the same techniques as the Model A on p. 37. The new tail elevator should be slid into the tail assembly slot using a sawing motion. Apply glue to the contact points after the tail is correctly centered and in position. Wheels should be mounted just in front of the lower wing on outside of the skid.

The Wright Exhibition Model of 1910 is a smaller version of the Model A-B, and can be built with one forward elevator. The Vin Fiz was a <u>*1911 Exhibition Model (Ex)*</u>. *Build using the Model B instructions. The tail assembly support should be 1 1/2", skids are 1 1/4".*

Wright 1910 Exhibition Model (Ex)

A, B are the wings.
C1-4 are the wing struts.
D1,2 are elevators (2nd is optional).
E1-4 are elevator struts.
F is the tail assembly.
G is the tail elevator.
H is the tail assembly top strap.
I is the landing skid frame.
J is the engine.
K1,2 are propellers.
L1,2 are propeller mounts.
M is the seat.
N1,2 are front stabilizers (see MoB).
O1,2 are wheels.
Tail assembly support toothpick is one and one-quarter inches.
Landing skids are 2 inches long.
Use A-B instructions for 1910 Ex.

81

Wright Model B

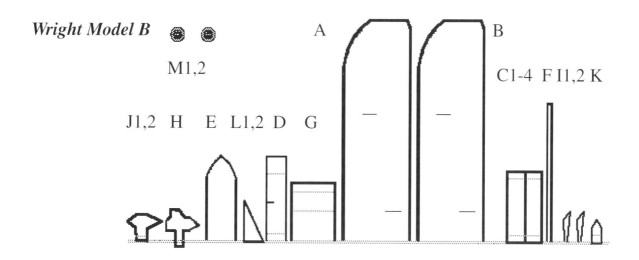

M1,2

J1,2 H E L1,2 D G   A   B   C1-4 F I1,2 K

Wright Model R Roadster   *Wright Baby Grand*

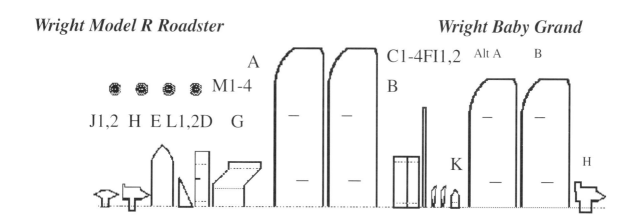

M1-4

J1,2 H E L1,2D G   A   C1-4FI1,2   B   Alt A   B   K   H

TA Wright Model B

A and B are the wings.

C1-4 are the wing struts.

D is the tail assembly.

E is the elevator.

F is the tail assembly top strap.

G is the landing skid frame.

H is the engine.

I1,2 are propellers.

J1,2 are propeller mounts.

K1,2 are seats.

L1,2 are front vertical stabilizers.

M1,2 are wheels.

Landing skid toothpicks are one and five-eighths inches long.

Tail assembly support is one and three-fourths inches long.

Wheels mount in front of the wing.

Use Mo A instructions except for upper air frame and stabilizers.

The most widely used of the new 1910 models, the Model B was the best and safest flyer of its time, and capable of 45 mph. The TA model has landing skids with two bends, one-eighth and one-quarter inch from the wide, front end of the skid. The upper airframe is glued on the skid ends, and clipped when dry. Add the front vertical stabilizers as shown.

The first Wright Roadster finished 3rd in the 1910 Gordon Bennet Trophy speed race. The TA Model R varies from the "B" in size and having four wheels. Two wheels should mount at the rear of the landing skid, the front 1/2 inch forward.

TA Wright Model R, Baby Grand

A and **B** are the wings.

C1-4 are the wing struts.

D is the tail assembly.

E is the elevator.

F is the tail assembly top strap.

G is the landing skid frame.

H is the engine.

I1,2 are propellers.

J1,2 are propeller mounts.

K is the seat.

L1,2 are front vertical stabilizers.

M1-4 are wheels.

Alt A, B, and **H** are Baby Grand pts.

Landing skids are one inch long.

Tail assembly support is 1-1/4".

Assemble the same as Model A, with one bend in skids.

Curtiss Model D, H1 Hydroaeroplane, Headless Pusher

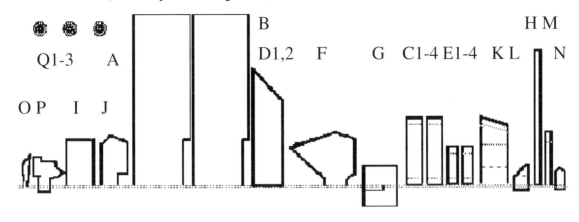

Wright Model C, C-Hydro

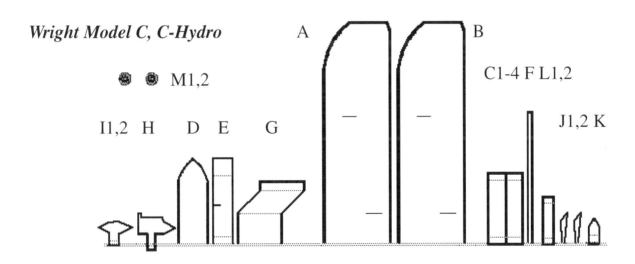

Curtiss Model D

D assembly requires 15 degree angle for the lower airframe tied together by part M for mounting the front elevator. Upper air frame protrudes one-eighth inch.

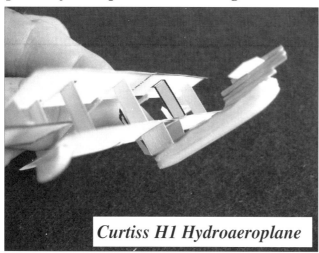

Curtiss H1 Hydroaeroplane

Headless Pusher

TA Curtiss Models D, H1 Hydro-aeroplane, and Headless Pusher.
A and B are the wings.
C 1-4 are wing struts.
D 1,2 are ailerons (protrude 3/8" beyond wingtips).
E 1-4 are aileron struts.
F is the tail plane/elevator.
G is the rudder.
H 1,2 are the tail assembly straps.
I is the Mo D elevator.
J is the Mo H1 elevator.
K is the landing gear assembly.
L is front landing gear assembly.
M is the Mo D elevator tie strap.
N is the seat.
O is the propeller.
P is the engine.
Q1-3 are wheels.
Tail assembly supports are 1-1/4". Lower air frames are 1-3/4". Cut upper air frames to project in front of elevator 1/4" for weight and bumper effect (Mo D only). Fuselage is 1" on Mo D, 1-1/2" on H1, 1-1/4" on Headless Pusher. *All three airplanes use aileron struts which mount to the upper wing trailing edge before mounting the upper wing to the lower. The H1 requires the landing gear assembly to be reversed, with the angled tips glued to the lower wing. This allows the fuselage to be mounted centrally under the assembly (K), with the float glued underneath. Cut float from styrofoam plate or meat tray. Use plastic cement for attaching float.*

Wright Model C & CH (Hydro)

A and B are the main wings.

C 1-4 are wing struts.

D is the tail plane.

E is the tail assembly.

F is the tail assembly top strap.

G is the landing skid frame.

H is the engine.

I 1,2 are propeller mounts.

J 1,2 are propellers.

K1,2 are seats.

L 1,2 are front vertical stabilizers.

M 1,2 are the wheels.

Landing skid toothpicks are 1-1/2" long with one bend for <u>Mo C</u>.

Landing skid toothpicks are 1-1/4" with no bend for <u>Mo CH</u>.

Tail assembly support is 1-3/4".

Use foam meat trays (after thorough cleaning) or foam plates for floats. Cut pontoon to width of landing skid frame (**G**). Use plastic model glue for foam to paper and wood connection.

Reverse the landing skid frame (**G**) so that "feet" are glued to wing.

Assemble with Model B instruc.

The styrofoam meat tray in background makes excellent pontoons for Wright and Curtiss float planes.

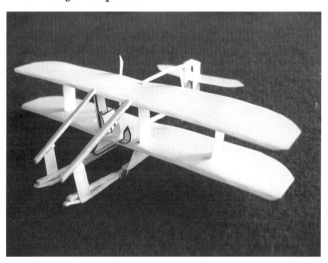

Wright Model C aircraft had the new 6 cylinder engine, and was fast and effective for the times.

Foam trays and plates have gently curved edges that make excellent floats or pontoons and are easily cut with scissors. Shape the edges and hollow the center to fit the fuselage with a sharp hobby knife.

Model CH had a large central float, small floats at wingtips.

The Curtiss Model D Type 4 at the right was the second airplane purchased by the US Army Signal Corps. It was accepted at Fort Sam Houston, Texas on 27 April, 1911. Derived from this type was the Curtiss H-1 Hydro, as well as the "Headless Pusher" racer of 1912. The term headless referred to the removal of the front elevator on both Curtiss and Wright pusher airplane designs of the era.

Curtiss Model D, model at Smithsonian.

The 1910 Wright Model B had the elevator at the rear of the aircraft.

Vin Fiz flew across the U.S. in 1911.

The US Army also purchased a pair of Wright Model Bs in 1911. The Model B was used to mount and fire the first machine gun, the first bomb site and bomb release, and the first radio installed in an American military airplane.

The Wright Baby Grand was a reduced wingspan Model R (Roadster) with a 60 hp V8. Orville flew it at over 72 mph before it crashed in high wind at Belmont in 1910.

The Wright 6 cylinder, 60 horsepower engine was introduced in 1911. The Model Ex was capable of 55 mph with the old engine, and over 60 mph with the 6/60. With the new engine, all the Wright aircraft were more competitive, though the light single seat Curtiss racers were still favored for speed. The 1911 headlines went to Cal Rodgers who flew his Vin Fiz across the U.S.

Lee-Richards

Annular Biplane

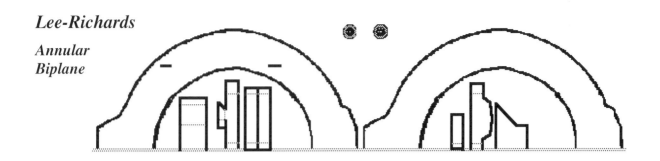

Beachy's Little Looper

The drawings on this page may be copied or scanned and printed with the author and BOOGER RED'S BOOKS INC. permission for the express and sole purpose of building TA aircraft.

A
H

B D

Q1-3

L E1-4 C1-4

K   F   G   P   O N

1912 Albatros Taube (Dove) Biplane

J1,2

A   g f   H

I1-4

B   C   d e

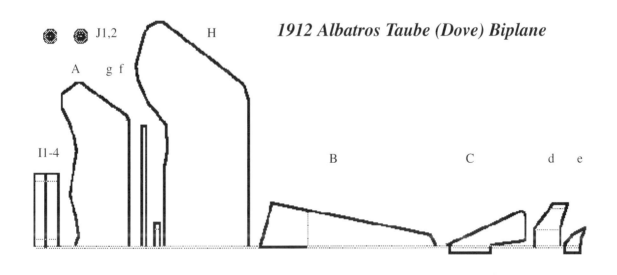

88

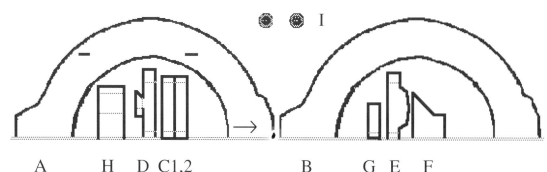

A   H   D C1,2   B   G E F

A is the top wing → leading edge.
B is bottom wing.
C 1,2 are outer wing struts.
D is the front center strut w/seat.
E is the tail rudder assembly.
F is the tail-plane/elevator.
G 1,2 are ailerons for front outer struts.
H is the landing gear assembly.
I 1,2 are wheels.
Skids and top fuselage are one inch long. Weight is 5/8" long.
Fuselage is one whole toothpick.

Lee-Richards Annular Biplane.

Add camber to bulged leading edge only. Assemble upper wing assembly (struts, front strut/seat, tail rudder, tail plane) with print side up. Do the same with the lower wing assembly, gluing central fuselage to lower side of wing with 1/8" overlap of rear wing. Landing gear assembly feet attach to lower wing. Do not press out camber when attaching upper, forward fuselage.

The Lee-Richards annular wing biplane was first built in 1910. It was actually developed and patented by GJA Kitchen of Lancaster. The design was unofficially dubbed "Kitchen's Doughnut" by the wise of the time.

Cedric Lee and G. Tilghman Richards (an engineer) continued to develop it as a monoplane for the next several years. In 1914 several versions were built, including 2 for the 1914 Gordon Bennet Trophy race. The type was very stable in the air, but just never became popular with fliers.

The TA Lee-Richards Annular Biplane is a flying replica of a non-flying replica built for the movie "Those Magnificent Men In Their Flying Machines." This airplane was included as challenge. While researching, I was told it would not fly. The design does fly well, but the wing and control surfaces are spread longitudinally, giving swift flat glides rather than loops or climbs and stalls.

Lincoln Beachy's Little Looper.

Lincoln Beachy's Little Looper was derived from the Curtiss Model D and Headless airplanes that Beachy had flown in his early years as a part of Glen Curtiss' Exhibition Team. According to at least one witness, in 1912 Beachy simply removed the front elevator from one of the Model D airplanes before flying and found the airplane performed better. The

Model D was the most popular American airplane and was built, modified, and imitated by hundreds of engineers, builders, fliers, and even backyard mechanics. Build the Little Looper using the same instructions as the Curtiss Headless Pusher, leaving ailerons to protrude only one fourth inch beyond the wing-tip.

Little Looper was specially modified with a larger tail plane/elevator and strengthened in every way because Beachy had heard that a Frenchman, Adolphe Pegoud, had looped the loop and flown upside down. Little Looper first flew in 1914. It was thought to be the best acrobatic aircraft of its time, and was powered by the 80 hp Gnome rotary engine at speeds up to 80 mph.

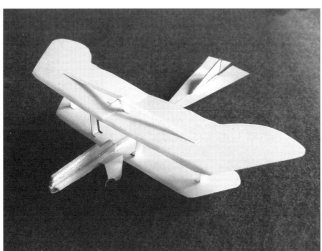

1912 Albatros Taube Biplane.

The Albatros Taube Biplane was derived from the popular Taube Monoplane and marked the first of a type of tractor biplane that was to dominate aircraft design in World War I. It employed the same type of wing warping for the trailing edge of the wing tips that the monoplane used. The Albatros Taube was powered by the 100 hp Argus engine, and was capable of 56 mph. The wing-span was 40 ft, and its length was 32 1/2 ft. This airplane was reputed to be capable of 19,000 ft in altitude, nearly impossible by 1912 standards. Build this airplane using Bleriot Monoplane instructions, adding the bottom wing as an assembly (tail and bottom wing mounted on fuselage) to the top wing assembly (wing and struts). It requires 8-1" toothpicks for balance.

Beachy-Eaton Monoplane

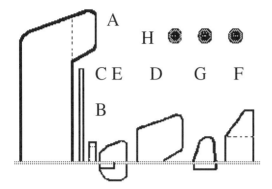

A

H

C E   D   G   F

B

Deperdussin Monoplane

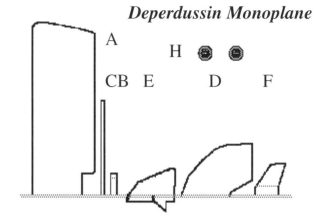

A

H

CB E   D   F

The parts list below has been standardized to apply only to the airplanes on this page.

A is the wing.

B is the wing brace.

C is the bracing strap.

D is the tail plane.

D-2 patch for Taube tail plane only, use after rudder assembly.

E is the tail rudder.

F is the landing gear.

G Beachy-Eaton front gear.

H are wheels.

Build all three using the Bleriot XI instructions except:

The telescoping tail on the Taube is similar to the Demoiselle (p.68), but the rudder slips in from the front.

Refer to photos on next page.

1911 Etrich Rumpler Taube (Dove)

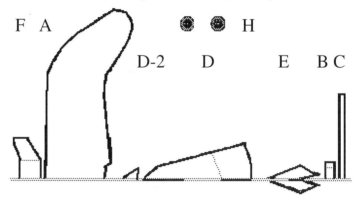

F A

H

D-2   D   E   B C

The Monoplane Was King

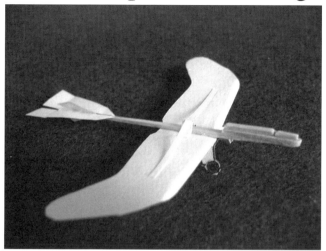

The TA Taube is a sleek and fast design.

The TA Deperdussin shows clean lines.

In 1912 Europe monoplane aircraft were winning endurance races, speed races, and were demonstrating the agility needed to thrill crowds at the exhibitions.

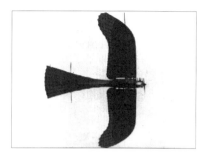

The Rumpler Taube in flight.

In Germany, the Taube or Dove was being produced by 10 different manufacturers, and with its 70 hp motor was considered a high performance airplane.

The Deperdussin monoplane was one of the most aerodynamically efficient airplanes of its time. A Deperdussin won the Gordon Bennet International Aviation Cup with a speed of 105.5 mph in 1912, beating the 1911 winner's (a Nieuport) speed of 78 mph.

Aerobatics and looping the loop were introduced to Europe by Adolphe Pegoud flying a Bleriot.

Lincoln Beachy, a Curtiss trained pilot, was Americas' first and foremost aerial acrobat, and the first to loop in the US. His advanced 1914 monoplane was his dream airplane, and it was capable of flying over 100 mph as well as performing aerial stunt flying.

TA Beachy-Eaton Monoplane.

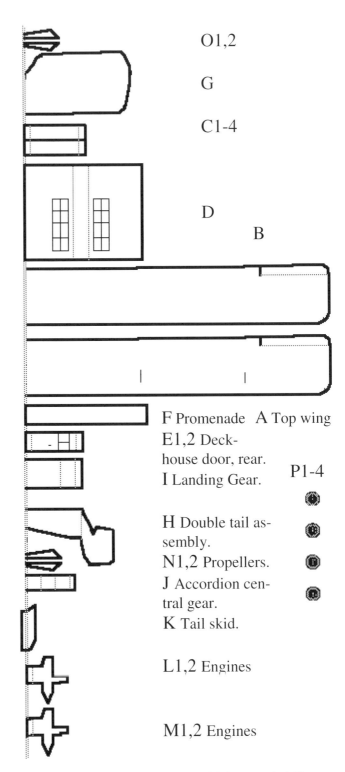

O1,2

G

C1-4

D

B

F Promenade A Top wing
E1,2 Deck-
house door, rear.
I Landing Gear.

P1-4

H Double tail as-
sembly.
N1,2 Propellers.
J Accordion cen-
tral gear.
K Tail skid.

L1,2 Engines

M1,2 Engines

A single full length sandwich toothpick is the fuselage. Four skids are 1 1/8 inch long. Landing gear assembly (**I**) mounts 1/8" from leading edge of bottom wing. Central skids mount on accordion (**J**). Mount-outside skids on (**I**) feet.

Mount the struts on the top wing as usual, but the deckhouse straddles the fuselage like an inverted U, viewed from the front. The promenade should be glued to one side of the fuselage front, then wrapped around the front and glued (cut to fit). Assemble as monoplane, then add top wing, then add engines.

Sikorsky's Grand Aeroplane.

The Russian Grand first flew in May 1913, and was destined to be the prototype of the heavy bombers of World War I. Igor Ivanovich Sikorsky designed and built the airplane himself. Previously, Sikorsky had established himself as a credible airplane designer with a series of single engined pusher airplanes. While building, locals called the Grand the "Petersburg Duck." After it was demonstrated, skepticism turned to awe and the "Duck" became the "Russkyi Vitiaz" (Russian Knight).

In its final form, the Grand had an 88 ft. wingspan and was 65 ft long. It was powered by 4 100 hp Argus engines mounted on the leading edge of the wings with tractor driven propellers. The Grand had a heated, enclosed deckhouse, with a pantry, toilet, and comfortable furnishings for long distance flying. An outside "promenade" deck made the Grand truly grand. The Grand was the largest airplane in the world, and could carry more passengers in comfort over greater distances than any other plane in 1913. It was truly an air-ship!

The TA version is a little more complicated to build than some of the TA Airforce because of the additional parts for the enclosed cabin and promenade deck. The TA Grand makes long smooth glides and has adjustable wing tip ailerons. The Grand is built in a smaller scale than the other flyers. It would have a wing-span of more than 11 inches if the same scale had been applied.

Igor Sikorsky was inspired by Jules Verne's writing and the wonderful inventions he foresaw.

Women Fliers and Danger

In *Proving They Fly* we describe the airplanes and builders, but the fliers themselves were the key to the future. For the men and women that flew in exhibitions the danger was intense. While in 1909 there were relatively few accidents, from 1910 on pilots pushed their airplanes to new extremes. John Moisant, who placed second in the 1910 Gordon Bennet Trophy Race, was killed within a year of his victory. Ralph Johnstone, the Wright trained pilot who had survived crashing the Baby Grand racer at the same race, was killed within weeks. In Europe it was the same, and no matter who built the airplanes, the trend would continue. Exhibition flying was killing and maiming pilots at a great rate, making flying dangerous as an occupation or sport. It would become even more dangerous as airplanes began going farther, faster, and higher.

Lincoln Beachy was killed in his monoplane.

But perhaps the danger was part of the attraction. New pilots flocked to the schools, and backyard experimenters continued to teach themselves to fly as well as build their own airplanes.

Among the new fliers were women; they were determined to take the risks associated with flight as part of the adventure. Blanche Scott was the first American woman to fly solo. Scott had enrolled in Glenn Curtiss' flight school. On September 2, 1910, she took off on her own. In fact, in those days the big part of a pilot's training consisted of taxiing back and forth across the training field. A governor was supposedly in place on the engine to prevent the novice from actually leaving the ground. Somehow the governor must have failed (Scott claimed innocence). Scott took off and flew before anyone could stop her, and later explained "a gust of wind had lifted her off." Scott went on to become a member of the Curtiss Exhibition Team, and later flew the "Red Devil" Curtiss type airplane that Thomas Baldwin built and made famous.

Bessica Raiche soloed two weeks after Blanch Scott in a Wright type biplane that she and her husband (a French aviator) built in their living room.

The first woman in the U.S. to win a pilots license was Harriet Quimby. She and John Moisant's sister, Matilde, had enrolled in the Moisant Aviation School on Long Island in 1911. Quimby had 33 lessons in a version of the famous Bleriot, and got license #37 in August of 1911. Matilde followed suit two weeks later. Both flew in air shows across America in 1911 and 1912. Quimby became famous as the first woman to fly the English Channel.

TROUBLE SHOOTING

Trouble shooting for TA airplanes can seem complicated. There is good reason for this. As the TA airplanes become more complicated, they produce more drag. Even lift produces drag. Drag produces similar problems in terms of tuning the wing (or wings) of your flyer that lift produces, without the lift. It's a double whammy! While attempting to make each side of an aircrafts wings produce equal lift (and drag) is easy on paper, in reality it requires concentration and attention to minute detail. Even then, sometimes simple experimentation is the only way to address problems that are difficult to spot.

In other words, if the camber appears equal, and the left and right wings appear to have an identical angle of approach, try twisting (gently) the wing on the side that has more lift both up and down, flying your plane in between to gage the results. Look carefully at both the leading and trailing wing surfaces. Likewise, try adding or removing some of the camber effect (remove camber by reducing the camber fold slightly) on both wings, flying your glider with each change to observe the effect.

Another area requiring experimentation is weight for bringing the center of balance forward in your glider. While TA gliders can fly excellently with a little weight, sometimes more can make them fly better and faster. Use the elevator to compensate for increased weight.

Address questions or comments to the author, P.O. Drawer G, Clifton, Co. 81520. Plans for additional TA airplanes are available on inquiry.

Approximate Metric Conversion Table for Construction of TA Aircraft:

2 1/4"	= 5.8 cm	7/8"	= 2.3 cm
2"	= 5.1 cm	3/4"	= 1.9 cm
1 3/4"	= 4.5 cm	5/8"	= 1.6 cm
1 5/8"	= 4.2 cm	1/2"	= 1.3 cm
1 1/2"	= 3.9 cm	3/8"	= 1 cm
1 3/8"	= 3.5 cm	1/4"	= 7 mm
1 1/4"	= 3.2 cm	3/16"	= 5 mm
1 1/8"	= 2.9 cm	1/8"	= 4 mm
1"	= 2.6 cm	1/16"	= 2 mm

The metric conversion table above is adapted for the purpose of building TA airplanes! It may not reflect exact measures, instead it rounds measures for the express purpose of maintaining the balance and structures of TA aircraft. It is included only for the use of those who prefer to use metric measure.

CONCLUSION

In BUILD AND FLY THE FIRST FLYERS I have selected airplanes that were pivotal in the developmental, pioneering years of flight. While other airplanes were important, and I may have wished to include more or different aircraft, these were the most representative of the era. They demonstrate the alternative technologies that were available, and the first real solutions to the problems of controlled, powered flight.

Readers are encouraged to research and build TA replicas of those airplanes not included. The formulas you master by building and tuning the airplanes in this book can be applied to any airplane that ever flew, or even to many of those which may not have. I did not include Whitehead's #21, or Langley's Aerodrome and others deliberately, because they lacked one or more of the essentials for powered, controlled flight. TA versions of these airplanes can be made to fly, although an adequate vertical tail and rudder must be added to #21. The drawings in this book come from many sources (see *Sources and Recommended Reading*), but you can make your own drawings from silhouettes or actual plans of your own favorite airplane.

As a history, this book was intended to introduce the reader to the world's first airplanes. The brief history of the pioneer and inspiration for building the original should lend a frame of reference. I found the history of the era's pilots and planes fascinating as well as exciting. Hopefully readers will be inspired by their new ability to create a flying glider replica of these airplanes to read and research the pioneers and times further.

Glossary

Aerodynamics—The study of air in motion and the forces that act on solid surfaces that move through it. The word comes from the Greek terms *aer,* meaning air, and *dynamis,* meaning "power."

Aileron—A control surface set into or near the wing tips, used to control the longitudinal axis of the airplane. Ailerons are connected, so that when one is extended up, the opposite wings aileron is extended downward. Ailerons were developed from the Wright concept of wing warping, which increases the lift on one side while simultaneously reducing it on the other.

Airfoil—A surface or body, like a wing, propeller blade, rudder, or aileron, designed to obtain a reaction of lift, drag, or thrust when it moves through the air.

Airplane and aeroplane—An airplane is a heavier-than-air craft that can be propelled through the air supporting itself on the lift from its wings. The British and some Europeans still use the term aeroplane.

Angle of attack—The acute angle between the chord of an airfoil, and a line representing the undisturbed relative airflow.

Aspect ratio—The ratio between the span of a wing and its chord. A high aspect ratio wing (longer, narrow wing) can achieve more lift from the same wing area because of reduced drag.

Drag—A resistant force exerted in a direction opposite to the direction of motion and parallel to the relative air stream. Three kinds of drag affect flight; profile drag, caused by the shape of or profile of the airplane wing. Induced drag is a bi-product of the wings lift. Parasite drag is resistance from parts of the airplane other than the lifting surfaces.

Fuselage—The fuselage is the body of the airplane. The word comes from the French word *fusele,* meaning "spindle shaped."

Four forces of flight—There are four forces that affect flight, gravity, lift, drag, and thrust.

Parts of an airplane—Fuselage, wings, tail assembly, engine, propellers, and landing gear. A glider is an airplane technically, even though it has no engine.

Types of lift—Dynamic lift is the force created by the movement of an airfoil or wing through the air irrespective of camber. Induced lift is the additional force created by the effect of a cambered airfoil.

Tail Assembly—The tail assembly is at the rear of the fuselage. It is sometimes called the empennage, from the French word *empenner,* "meaning to feather the arrow."

Sources and Recommended Reading:

Listed alphabetically, by title.

Airplanes Of The World. By Douglas Rolfe and Alexis Dawydoff. Simon and Schuster 1962.

Flight. By John W. R. Taylor. Peebles Press International Inc. 1974.

Janes Fighting Aircraft of WWI. The Military Press. Crown Publishers 1990.

Kill Devil Hill. By Harry Combs. Houghton Mifflin Company 1979.

The First Aviators. By Curtis Prendergast. Time-Life Books Inc. 1980.

The First To Fly. By Sherwood Harris. Simon and Schuster 1970.

The Rand McNally Encyclopedia of Military Aircraft. Edited by Enzo Angelucci. The Military Press. Crown Publishers, Inc. 1983.

The Road To Kitty Hawk. By Valerie Moolman. Time-Life Books 1980.

Understanding Flight. By David Anderson and Scott Eberhardt. McCraw-Hill 2000.

Wilbur and Orville. By Fred Howard. Alfred A. Knopf 1987.

Wright Brothers National Memorial. By Omega G. East. National Park Service Historical Handbook Series No 34.

The following journals provided valuable information and graphics.

AAHS Journal. American Aviation Historical Society.

WWI Aero. The Journal of the Early Aeroplane.

International AeroPlans. Edited by Andrew C. Anson.

Aviation History. Published bi-monthly by Cowles History Group.

The following source organizations are (as of 2001) found on the internet at:

Lincoln Beachy Web Site—http://www.lincolnbeachey.com
The Early Birds of Aviation—http://www.earlybirds.org
Wright Brothers Aeroplane Co.—http://www.wright-brothers.org

Visits to the following National Historic Sites and Museums provided photos and information as well as inspiration.

United States Air Force Museum at Dayton, Ohio.
The Wright Brothers National Memorial at Kitty Hawk, NC.
The Smithsonian's National Air and Space Museum.